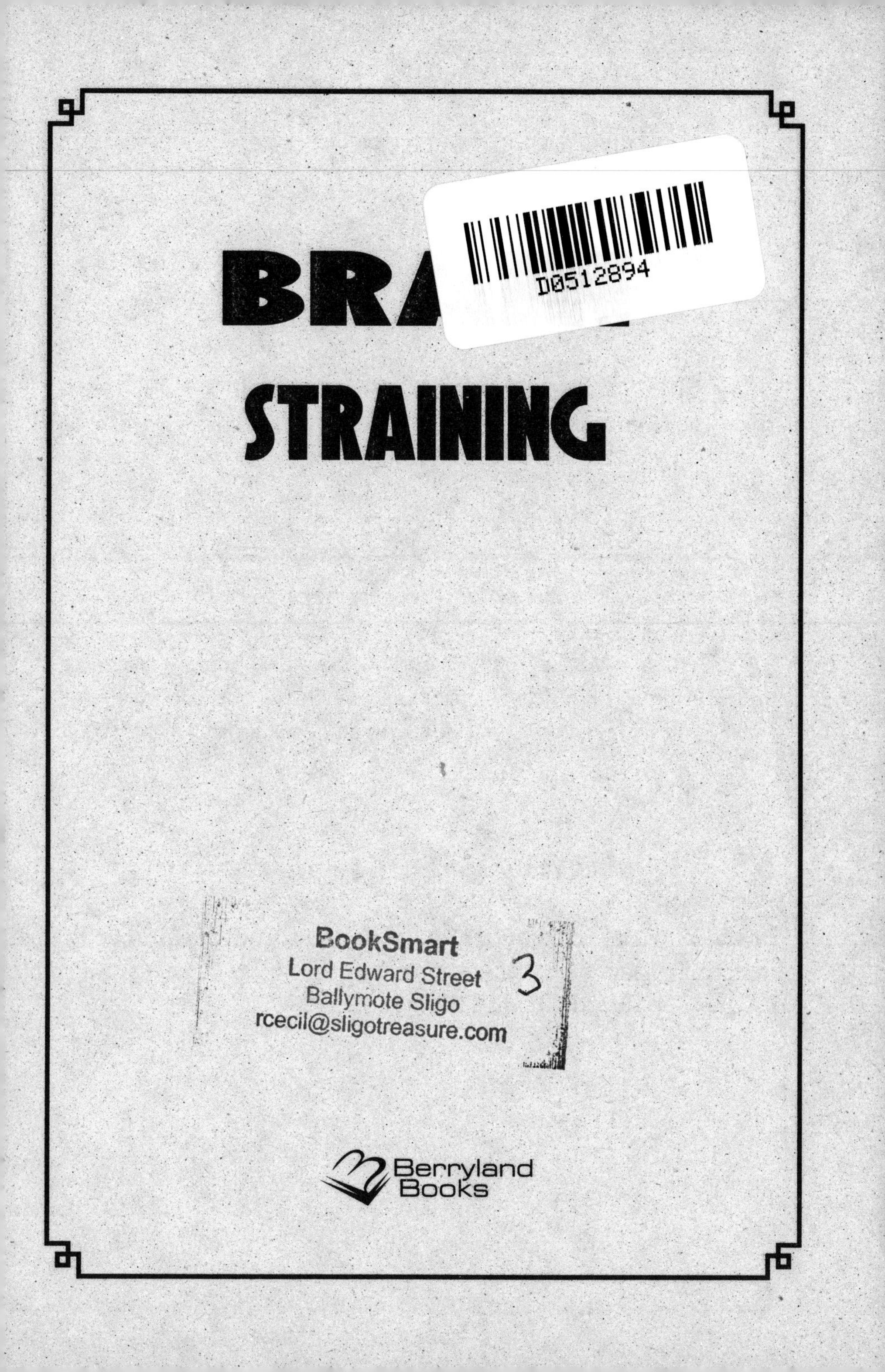
BRA
STRAINING
D0512894
BookSmart
Lord Edward Street
Ballymote Sligo
rcecil@sligotreasure.com
3
Berryland
Books

How to do Crosswords:

The goal of a crossword is to fill the available white squares, both vertical and horizontal, by solving the given clues. Some words overlap with others so pick your answers carefully!

How to do Wordsearches:

The object of a wordsearch is to find all the words hidden in a grid. These words may be hidden horizontally, vertically or diagonally. They may even have been written backwards!

How to do Sudoku:

The objective of Sudoku is to fill a 9x9 grid so that each vertical column, each diagonal row and each of the 3x3 smaller boxes contain the numbers 1 to 9 once only.

Easy SUDOKU

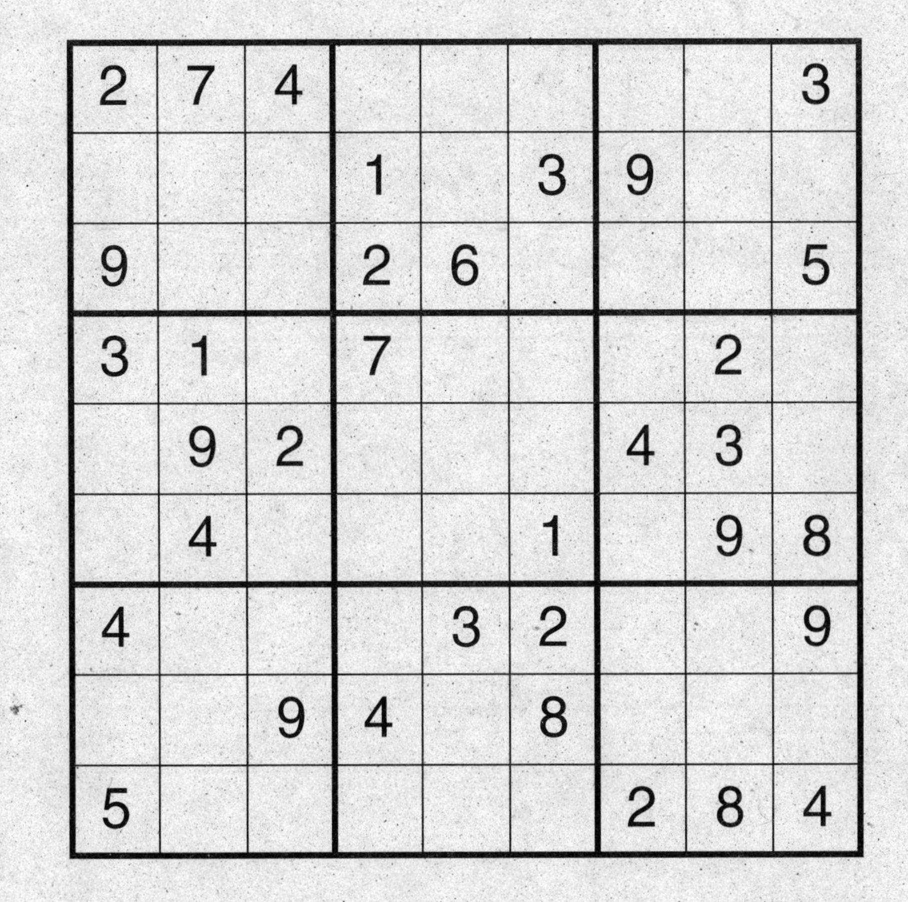

2	7	4						3
			1		3	9		
9			2	6				5
3	1		7				2	
	9	2				4	3	
	4				1		9	8
4				3	2			9
		9	4		8			
5						2	8	4

Easy SUDOKU

5	1	3	7			6		9
	8			5			7	4
6			1					3
				3		9		1
	6		9		5		8	
4		8		2				
7					3			5
8	3			1			4	
1		6			7	3	9	8

Easy SUDOKU

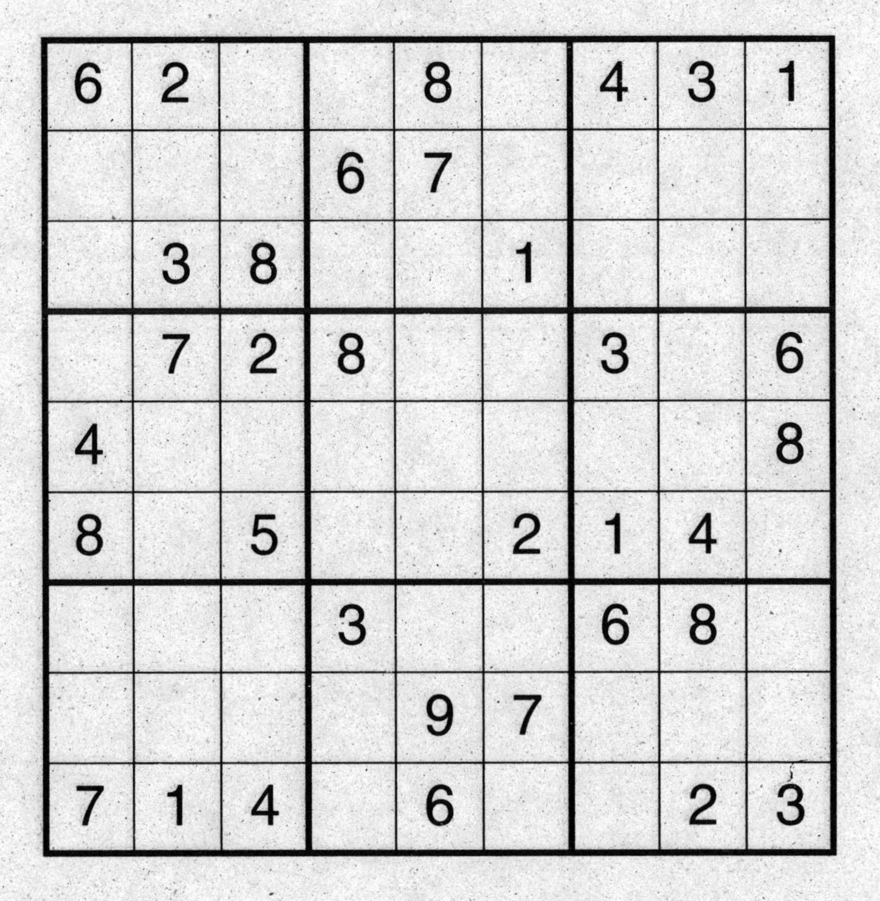

6	2			8		4	3	1
			6	7				
	3	8			1			
	7	2	8			3		6
4								8
8		5			2	1	4	
			3			6	8	
				9	7			
7	1	4		6			2	3

Easy SUDOKU

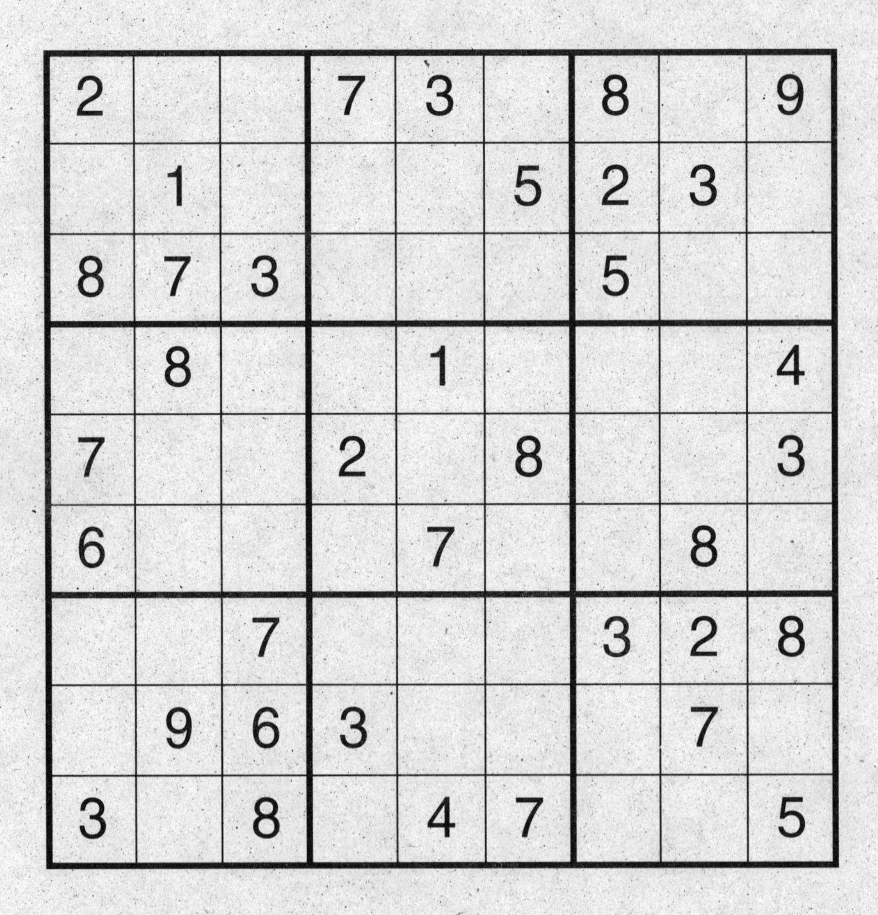

2			7	3		8		9
	1				5	2	3	
8	7	3				5		
	8			1				4
7			2		8			3
6				7			8	
		7				3	2	8
	9	6	3				7	
3		8		4	7			5

Easy SUDOKU

5		3	1	2				
					9	3		8
8				3		6		5
4	7	8		1				
3	5						7	1
				7		2	3	4
7		5		4				3
6		1	9					
				5	1	9		7

Easy SUDOKU

			3	1	6		9	
9		6		7		4	5	
3			4	9			1	
1					8		3	
		4	1		9	8		
	9		2					1
	3			2	4			5
	4	1		8		9		2
	7		9	5	1			

Easy SUDOKU

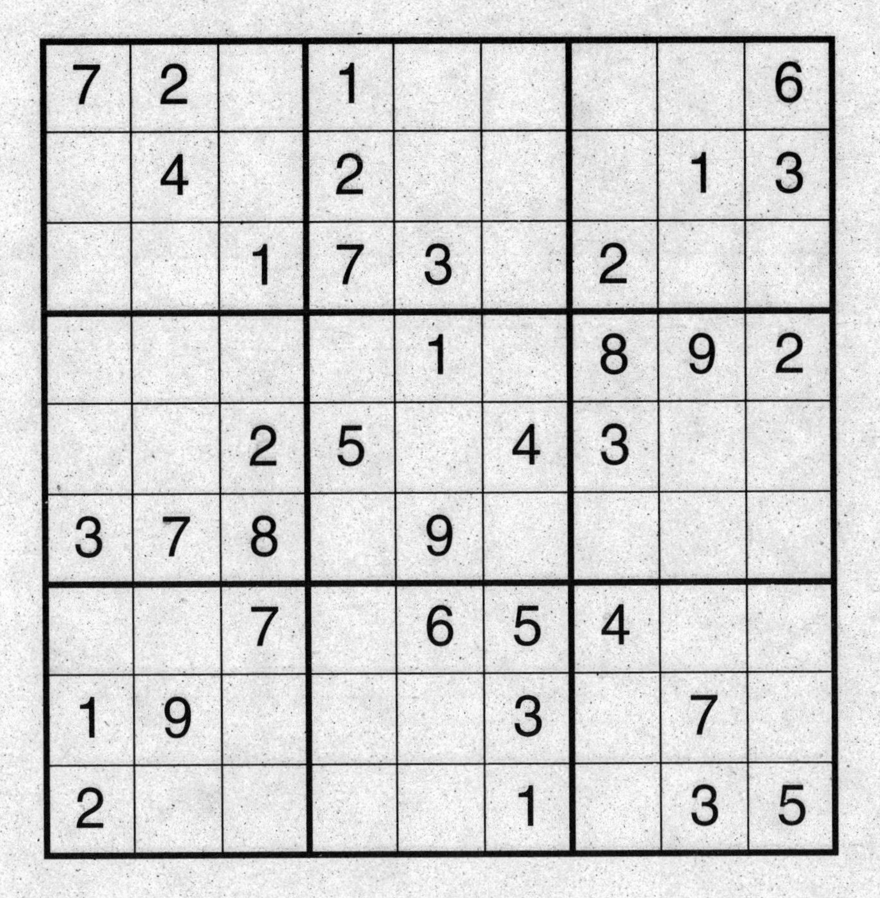

7	2		1					6
	4		2				1	3
		1	7	3		2		
				1		8	9	2
		2	5		4	3		
3	7	8		9				
		7		6	5	4		
1	9				3		7	
2					1		3	5

Easy SUDOKU

2	7				8		1	3
1		5	7					4
			2	1			7	
7				6		4	3	
		6	8		4	5		
	5	4		3				9
	2			5	9			
5					7	8		6
6	9		4				5	2

Easy SUDOKU

	8	2				9		
6				2	5	1		
	3	7			9			5
2			7		4			9
	7	8				5	6	
4			6		3			7
7			1			6	4	
		6	2	3				1
		1				7	9	

Easy SUDOKU

3	2			9			6	7
	7			8	6			
		1	5					2
2		6			4	7		1
		3				5		
4		8	7			6		9
1					5	4		
			8	3			9	
6	8			4			5	3

Easy SUDOKU

2		1	9	6				5
	5				3	7	4	
	3		5					9
	8			5		4		1
3			6		8			7
6		5		4			8	
5					6		9	
	9	8	2				7	
4				7	9	1		2

Easy SUDOKU

2	1		7				8	
					3	7	4	
			1			2		3
1		2		3		4		7
8	3						2	9
9		6		4		3		8
7		5			2			
	4	1	9					
	2				8		1	4

Easy SUDOKU

	5		2	8		9		
	6			3	1		5	7
8		9				4		
	8		5		7			2
5	7						9	4
4			3		6		7	
		2				6		5
6	3		8	1			4	
		8		5	9		3	

Easy SUDOKU

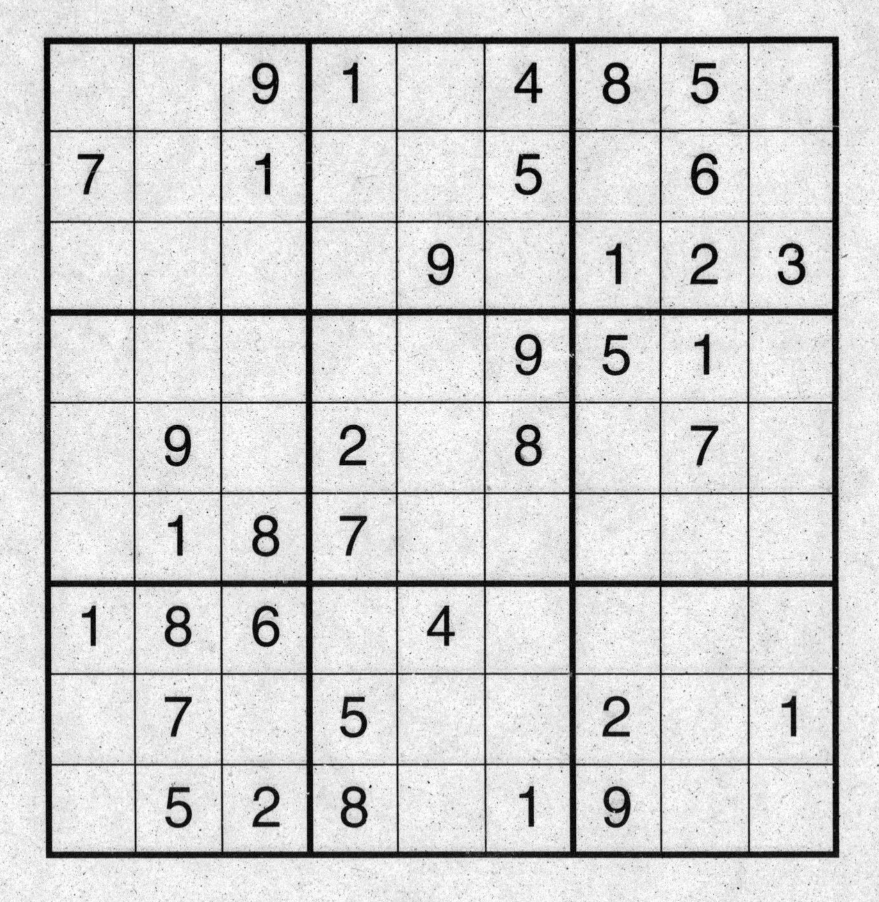

		9	1		4	8	5	
7		1			5		6	
				9		1	2	3
					9	5	1	
	9		2		8		7	
	1	8	7					
1	8	6		4				
	7		5			2		1
	5	2	8		1	9		

Easy SUDOKU

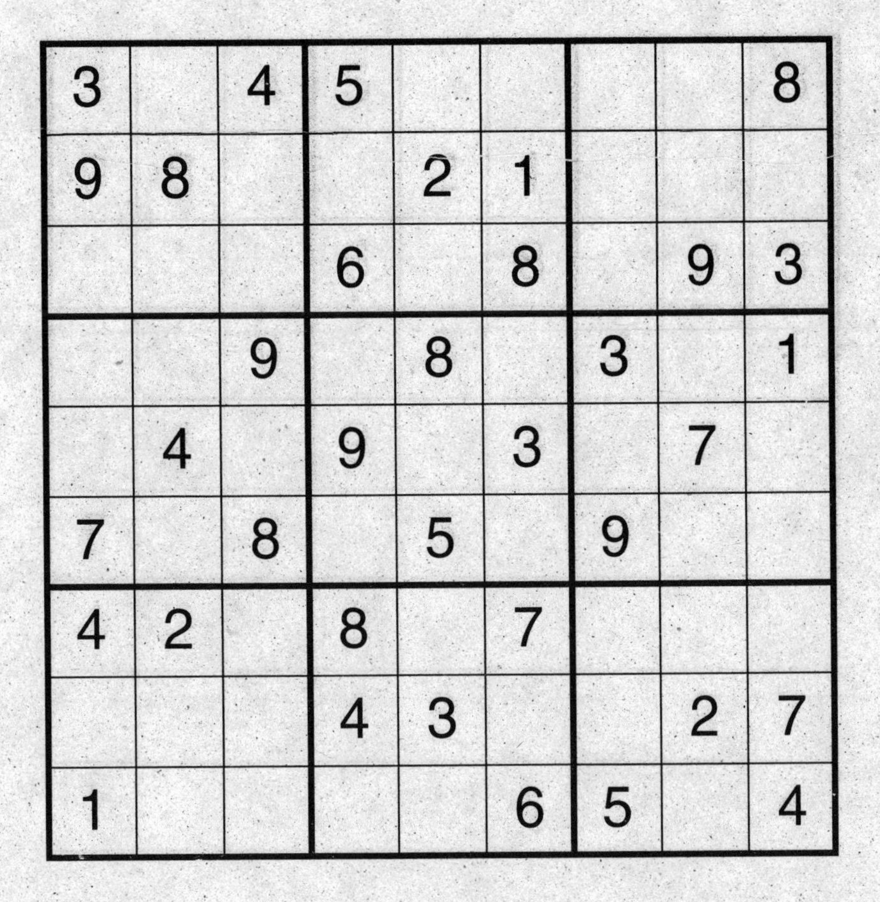

3		4	5					8
9	8			2	1			
			6		8		9	3
		9		8		3		1
	4		9		3		7	
7		8		5		9		
4	2		8		7			
			4	3			2	7
1					6	5		4

Easy SUDOKU

1		8		6	7			4
	6	3		1			7	
			8				1	9
8				5		7		
3	5		4		9		8	6
		2		7				3
5	8				1			
	7			9		4	3	
9			7	8		2		1

Easy SUDOKU

		6		1		5		
	4	5		2	3		9	
3				4			1	2
	7		1		2			
6	3	4				2	8	1
			4		6		3	
2	9			6				5
	6		5	7		8	2	
		1		9		3		

Easy SUDOKU

1		3	8			2		7
	8				2		3	
9				1	3			5
	2	1		6				8
		5	1		7	6		
6				9		1	7	
2			4	7				6
	3		5				1	
5		7			1	8		4

Easy SUDOKU

	3	5		1				9
2		4					5	8
			7		5	1		
	8	2		3	6			
5			1		2			6
			4	9		2	8	
		3	9		8			
4	2					8		1
6				7		9	3	

Easy SUDOKU

		2	9	3			7	
5		9			4	1		
	3				5		8	9
	9	8	5		1			2
2								6
6			2		9	8	1	
9	1		3				6	
		5	8			2		4
	2			9	7	5		

Easy SUDOKU

	4				2	9		
	6	2		9			8	3
7				8	3		5	
6		1	2		8			
	2	8				6	1	
			1		5	8		4
	7		8	3				9
3	8			1		5	6	
		6	5				3	

Easy SUDOKU

1		7	6			5		
	2			9			8	
	4			2	7	9		
9		3	4					
5	1	2				4	3	8
					3	1		5
		6	9	4			5	
	7			5			4	
		9			2	6		3

Easy SUDOKU

8					1		9	2
7		9	6			3		
	5			9	3		8	
6		5		7			3	
		7	1		5	9		
	9			4		5		8
	7		3	1			2	
		1			7	4		3
3	6		5					7

Easy SUDOKU

	9	7			1	2		
			7	9		8		1
1	3				6			5
6		3		1			2	
	5		8		9		6	
	7			4		5		3
3			9				5	2
7		8		6	5			
		9	1			6	7	

Easy SUDOKU

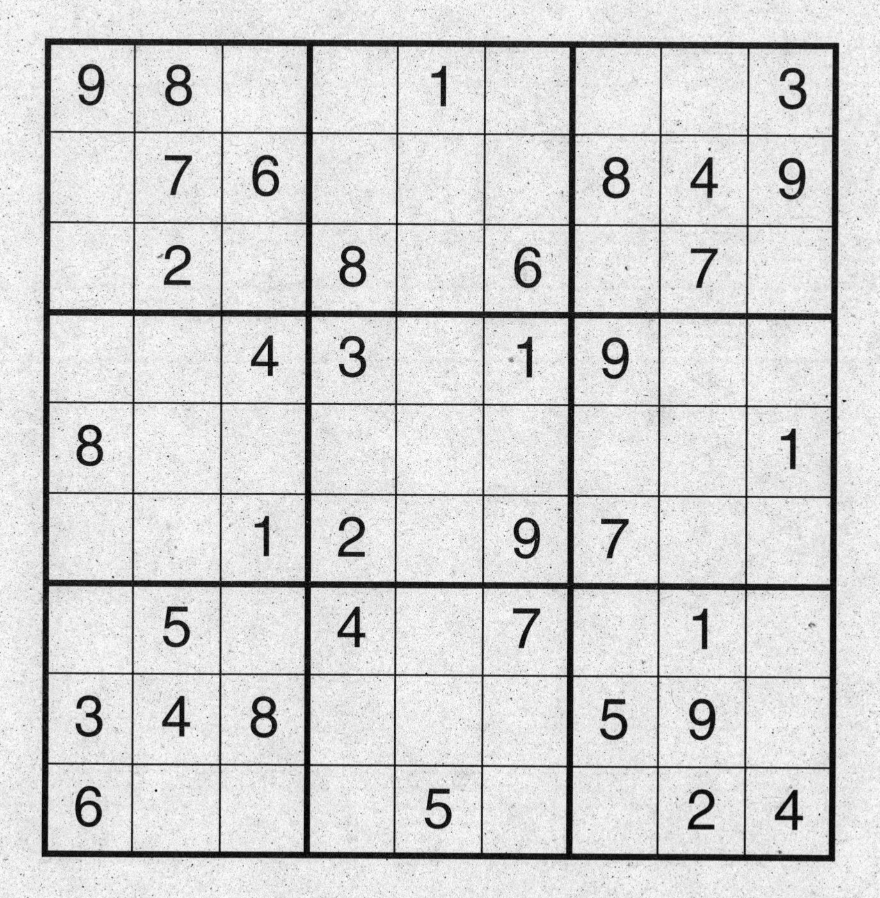

9	8			1				3
	7	6				8	4	9
	2		8		6		7	
		4	3		1	9		
8								1
		1	2		9	7		
	5		4		7		1	
3	4	8				5	9	
6				5			2	4

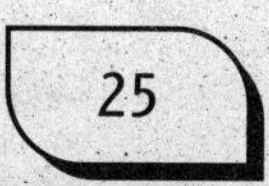

Easy SUDOKU

	4		6			1		2
1	7			9		4		
		3	1	4		9		
	6		4		8	2		3
	8						1	
2		1	3		6		4	
		2		3	9	5		
		6		8			9	1
4		7			1		2	

Easy SUDOKU

	2			4				
1	9	5	7	2				
					9	5	2	7
		6	5		7		8	
9			6		2			4
	8		4		1	3		
3	5	9	1					
				5	4	8	1	3
				7			6	

Easy SUDOKU

	3	8						7
9			7			5	6	
		5	9	2	6			
	5		6	9				
3	8	7				6	5	9
				7	5		1	
			4	8	7	2		
	9	4			2			3
8						4	7	

Easy SUDOKU

		4	1	2	8		3	
1				5		4		
	5				4			2
2		3	5		1			4
5	1						2	6
4			2		3	1		5
3			7				8	
		9		4				1
	7		8	9	5	2		

Easy SUDOKU

		3	6		4		9	
			9	5				1
7	9	5	2					
3		9	1	2			7	
	5	1				9	6	
	7			9	6	1		3
					1	3	2	4
5				4	2			
	1		7		9	6		

Easy SUDOKU

			8		9	2	6	
1		2		4				
6				3	2		5	
4		9	7		1			6
	6	5				1	7	
7			4		5	9		2
	7		3	5				9
				1		8		3
	3	8	6		4			

Easy SUDOKU

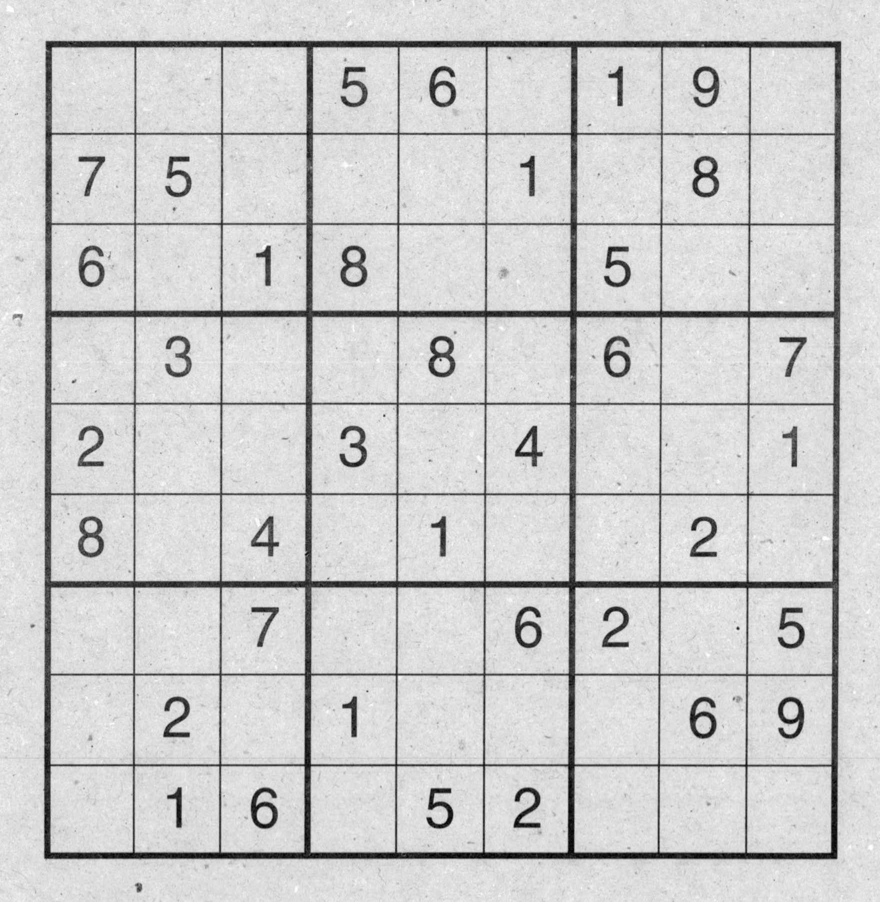

			5	6		1	9	
7	5				1		8	
6		1	8			5		
	3			8		6		7
2			3		4			1
8		4		1			2	
		7			6	2		5
	2		1				6	9
	1	6		5	2			

Easy SUDOKU

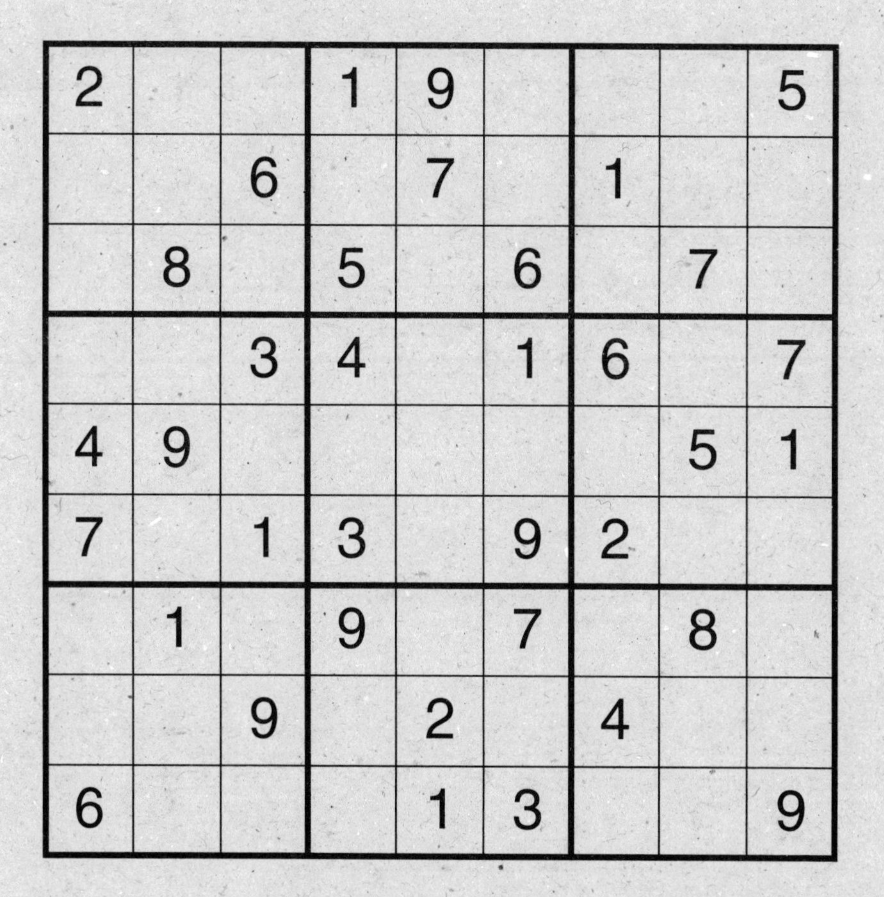

2			1	9				5
		6		7		1		
	8		5		6		7	
		3	4		1	6		7
4	9						5	1
7		1	3		9	2		
	1		9		7		8	
		9		2		4		
6				1	3			9

Easy SUDOKU

		6	9		4		1	
4	8					9	5	
	1	3			6	4		7
2		9		4				1
			5		9			
1				7		5		3
8		1	3			7	2	
	2	5					3	9
	9		1		7	8		

Easy SUDOKU

				4	2	9		
	4	2	5				1	
7		9			8	5	4	
5		8	2		9		3	
3								8
	2		3		4	6		9
	1	5	8			3		4
	8				1	7	2	
		3	9	2				

Medium SUDOKU

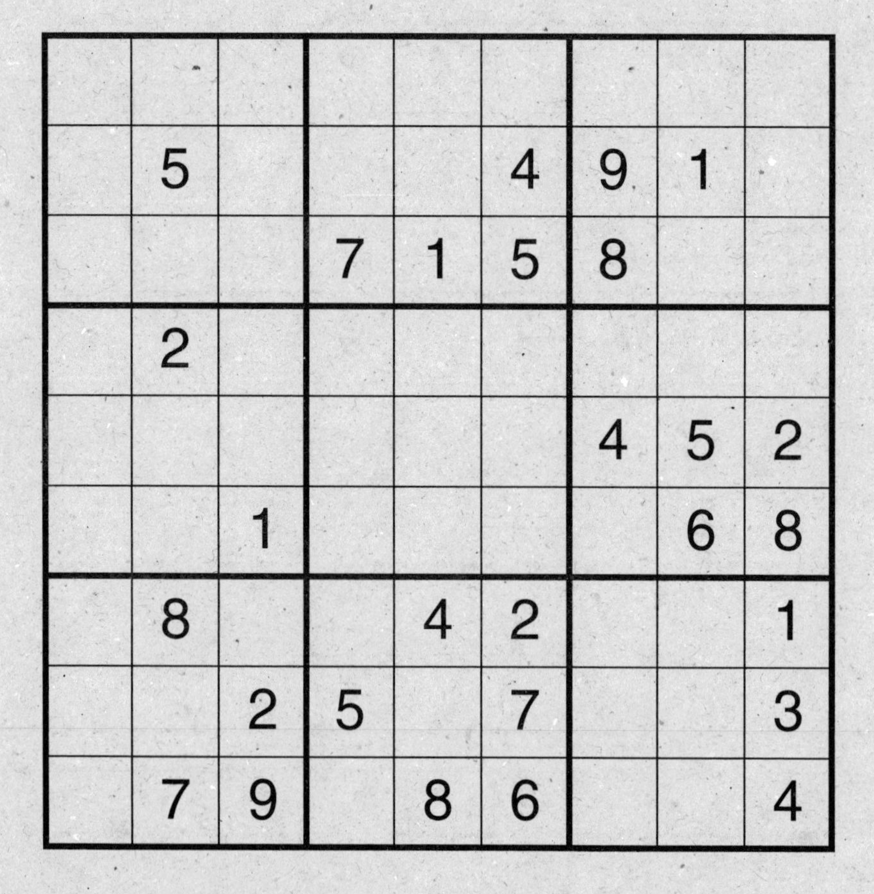

	5				4	9	1	
			7	1	5	8		
	2							
						4	5	2
		1					6	8
	8			4	2			1
		2	5		7			3
	7	9		8	6			4

Medium SUDOKU

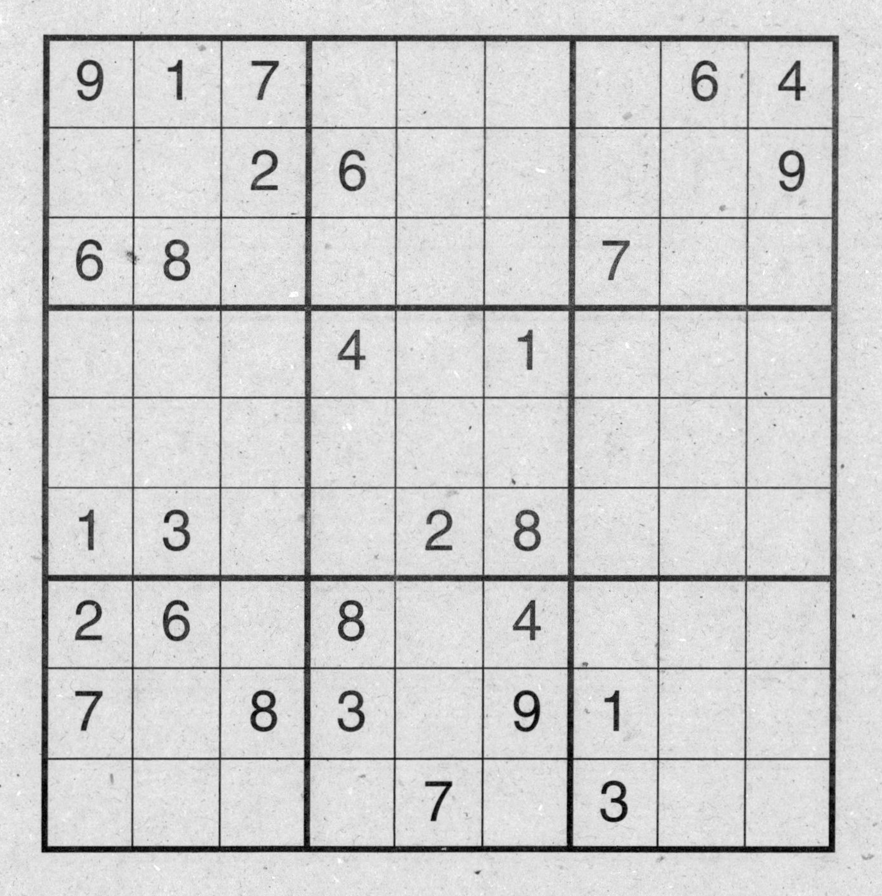

9	1	7					6	4
		2	6					9
6	8					7		
			4		1			
1	3			2	8			
2	6		8		4			
7		8	3		9	1		
				7		3		

Medium SUDOKU

	5	8						
2	3	6						
9								
			3	9				1
	8	3			4		5	9
		2	1	7				3
8	6				1	4		
		9	4					
	4			3		2		6

Medium SUDOKU

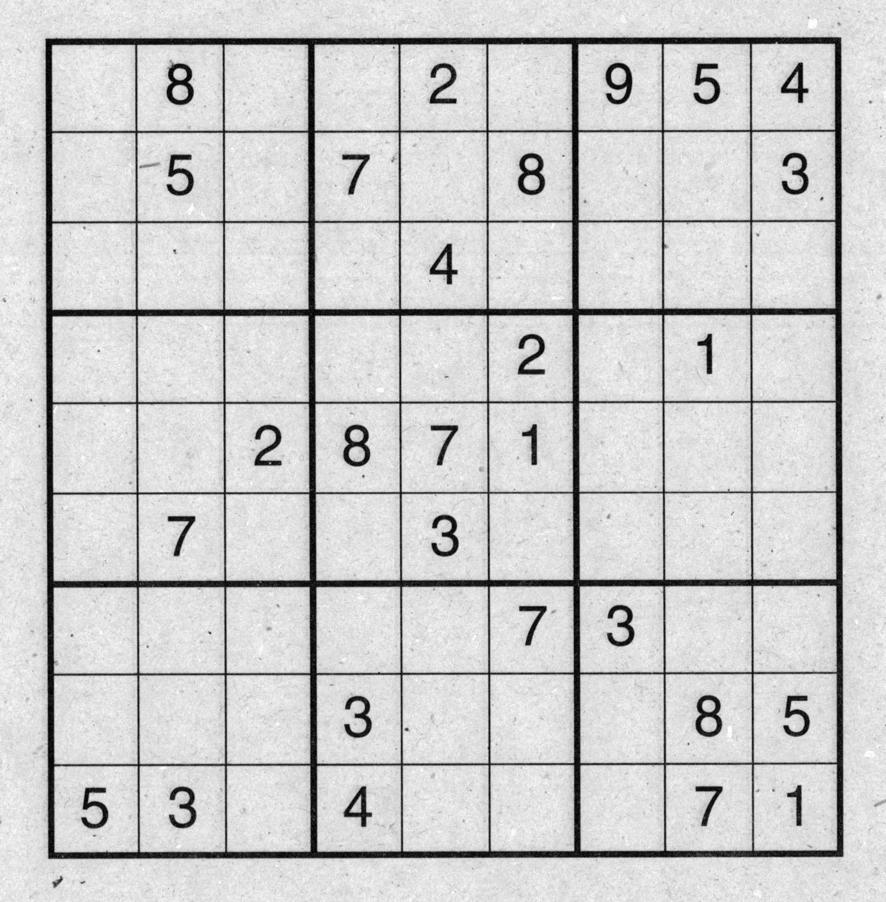

	8			2		9	5	4
	5		7		8			3
				4				
					2		1	
		2	8	7	1			
	7			3				
					7	3		
			3				8	5
5	3		4				7	1

Medium SUDOKU

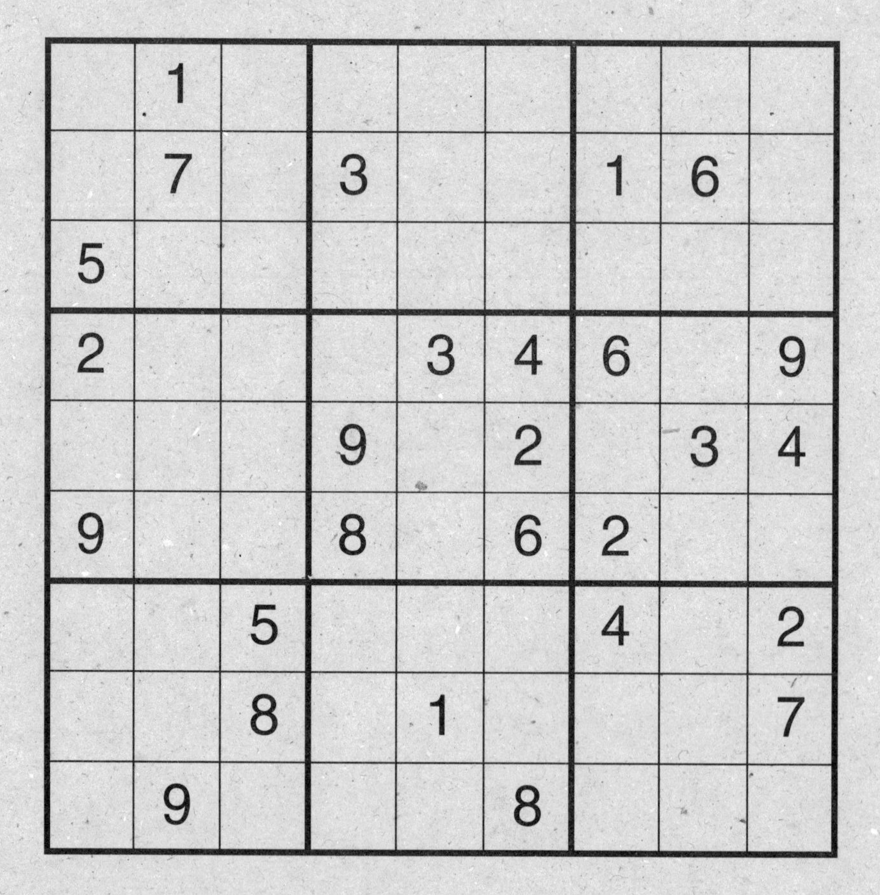

	1							
	7		3			1	6	
5								
2				3	4	6		9
			9		2		3	4
9			8		6	2		
		5				4		2
		8		1				7
	9				8			

Medium SUDOKU

3		7					9	
4		2		6			3	
	9		4		8		1	
2	3					1		
				4	3		2	7
	7	8	5					
		5	6		4			
			2	7	1			

Medium SUDOKU

5	6	4						
9					6	2	7	
		7						4
				3		1		2
4				8		3		
						4		
6			3	7				9
			6		8		1	
7	1		5				2	

Medium SUDOKU

		9	2					
2			3	9	6	1		
5								
			9	4		8		
		7			1	2		3
			6		7	9	1	
1	5							
9		8	7	2				
					5		9	

Medium SUDOKU

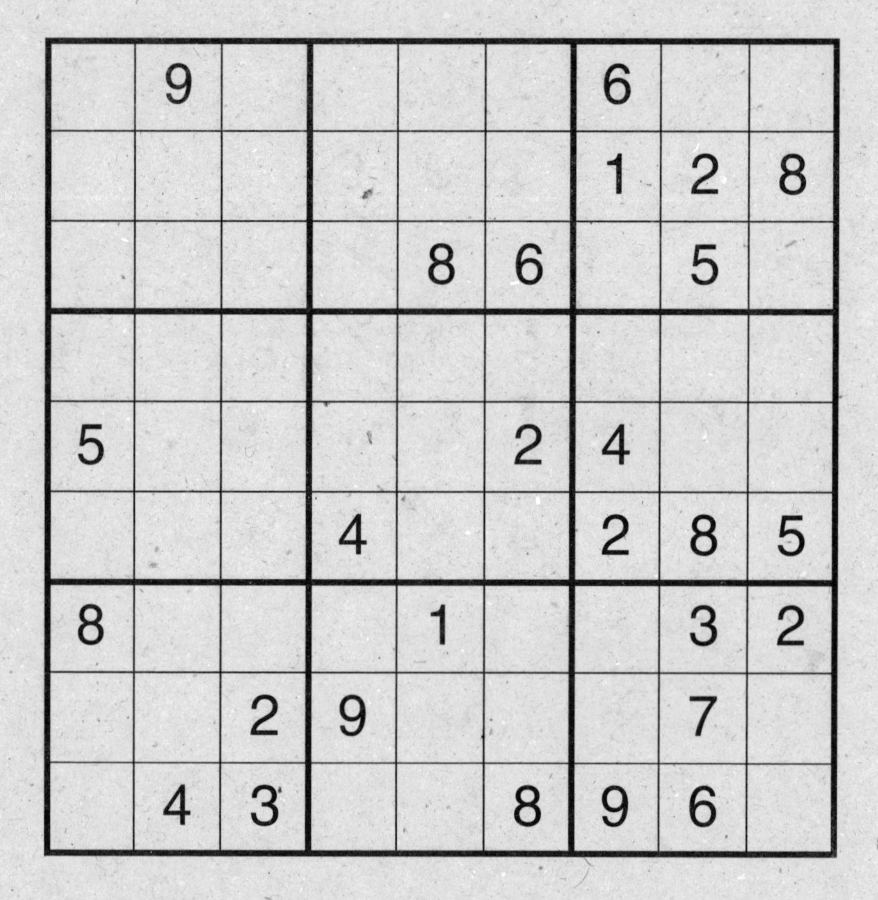

	9					6		
						1	2	8
				8	6		5	
5					2	4		
			4			2	8	5
8				1			3	2
		2	9				7	
	4	3			8	9	6	

Medium SUDOKU

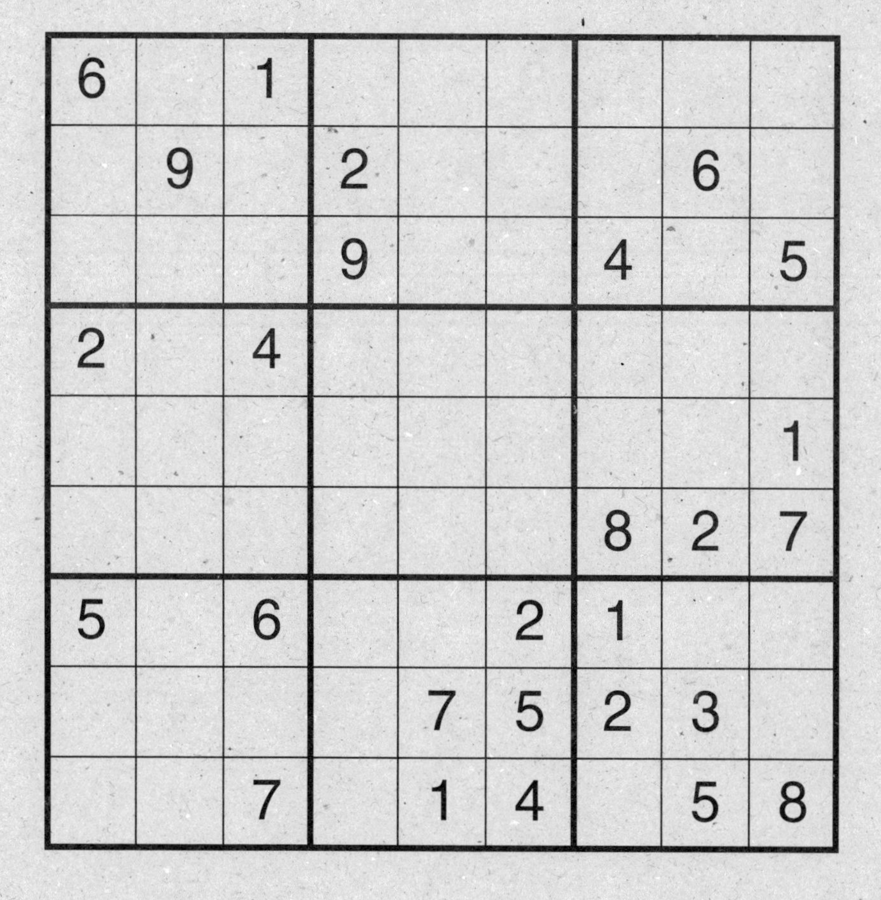

6		1						
	9		2				6	
			9			4		5
2		4						
								1
						8	2	7
5		6			2	1		
				7	5	2	3	
		7		1	4		5	8

Medium SUDOKU

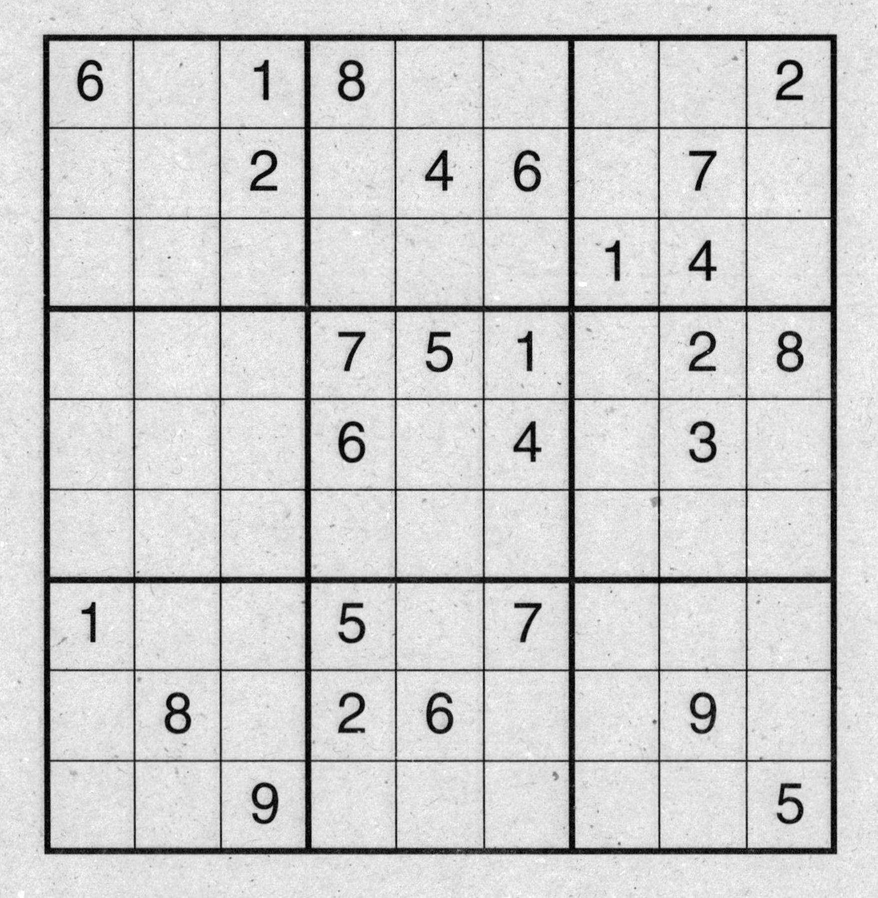

6		1	8					2
		2		4	6		7	
						1	4	
			7	5	1		2	8
			6		4		3	
1			5		7			
	8		2	6			9	
		9						5

Medium SUDOKU

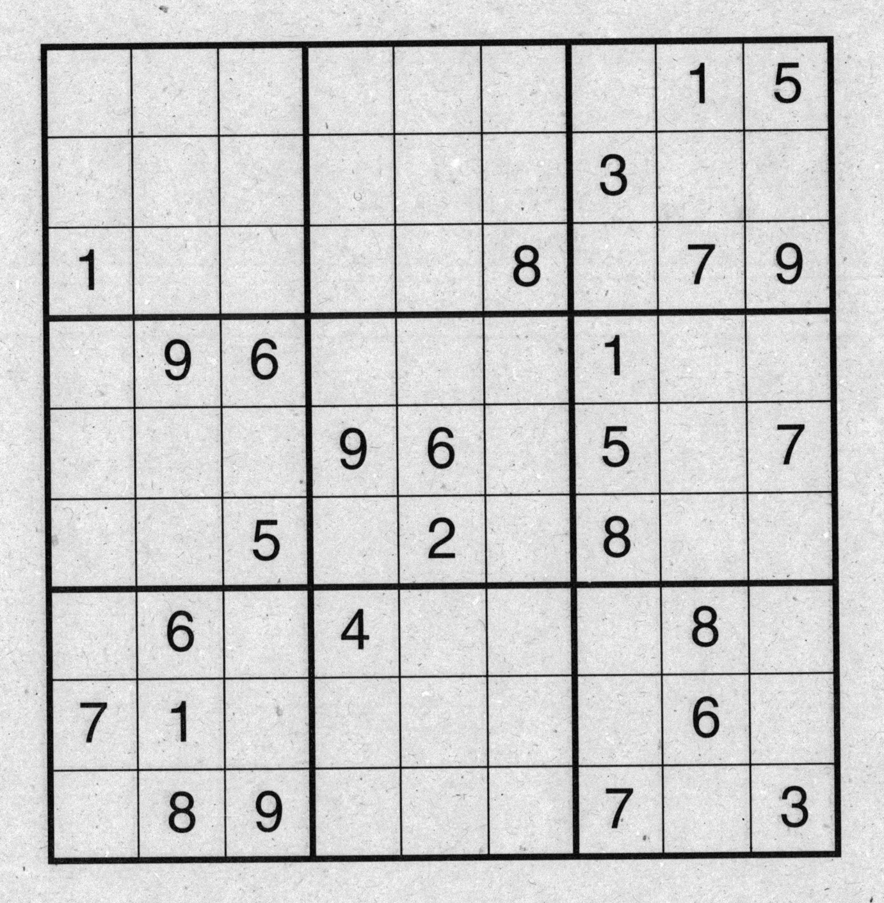

							1	5
						3		
1					8		7	9
	9	6				1		
			9	6		5		7
		5		2		8		
	6		4				8	
7	1						6	
	8	9				7		3

Medium SUDOKU

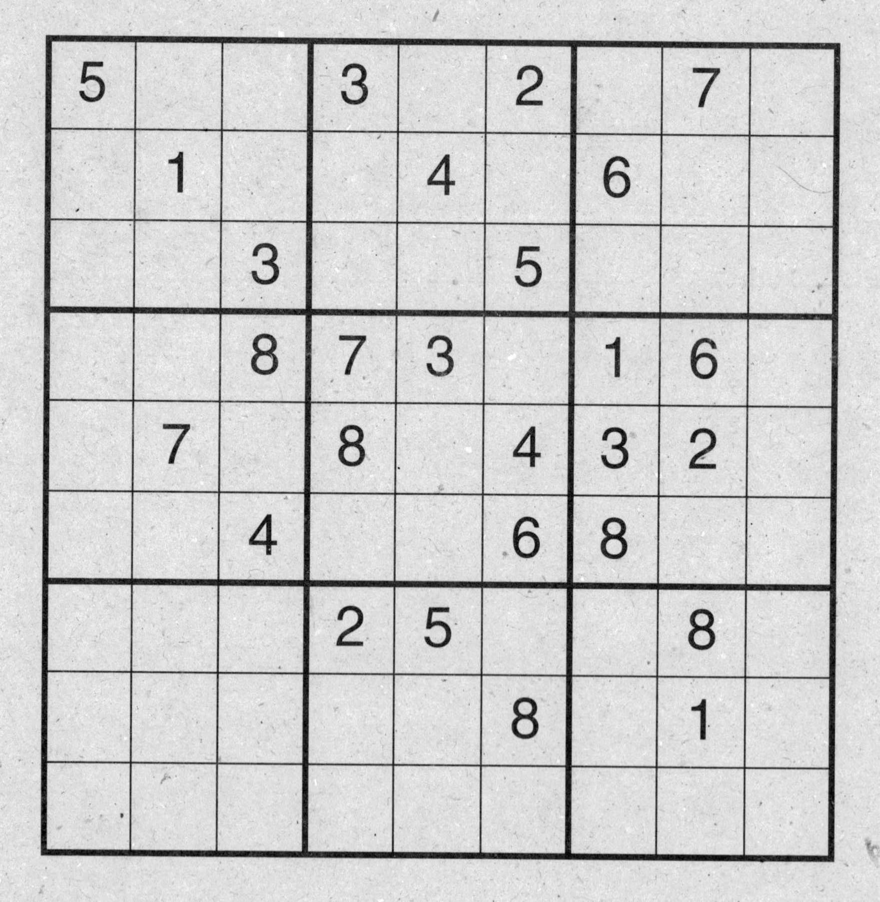

5			3		2		7	
	1			4		6		
		3			5			
		8	7	3		1	6	
	7		8		4	3	2	
		4			6	8		
			2	5			8	
					8		1	

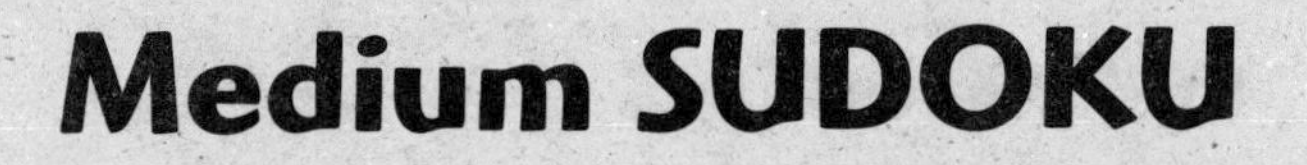

Medium SUDOKU

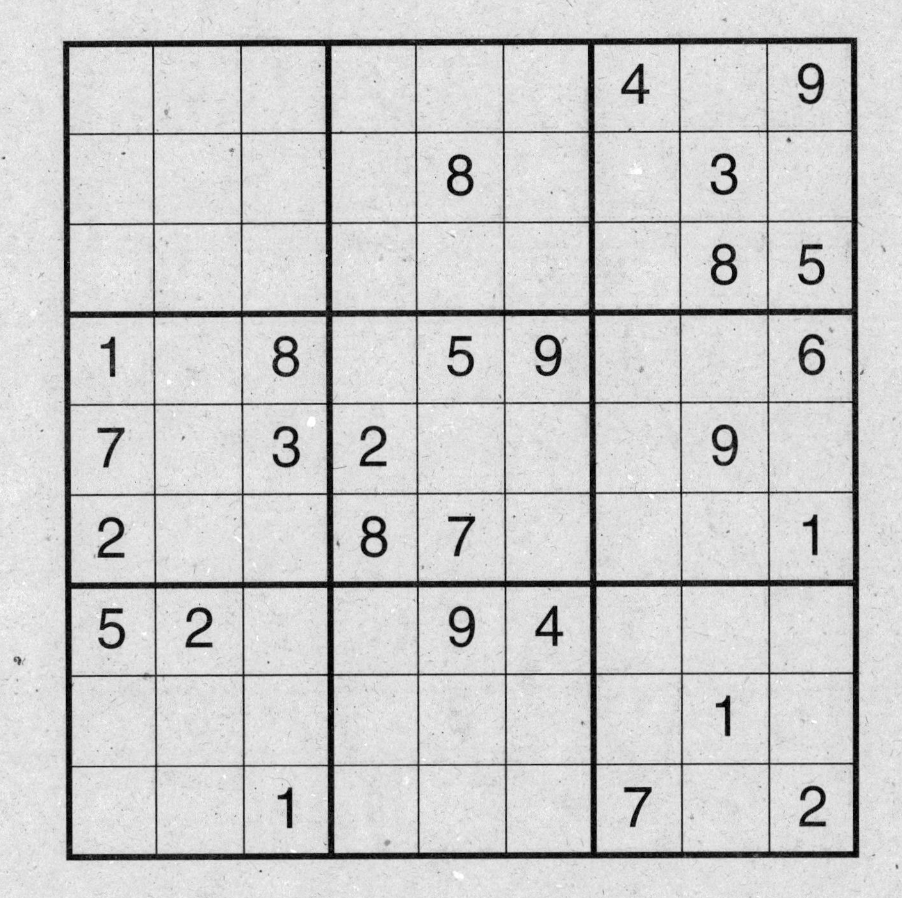

						4		9
				8			3	
							8	5
1		8		5	9			6
7		3	2				9	
2			8	7				1
5	2			9	4			
							1	
		1				7		2

Medium SUDOKU

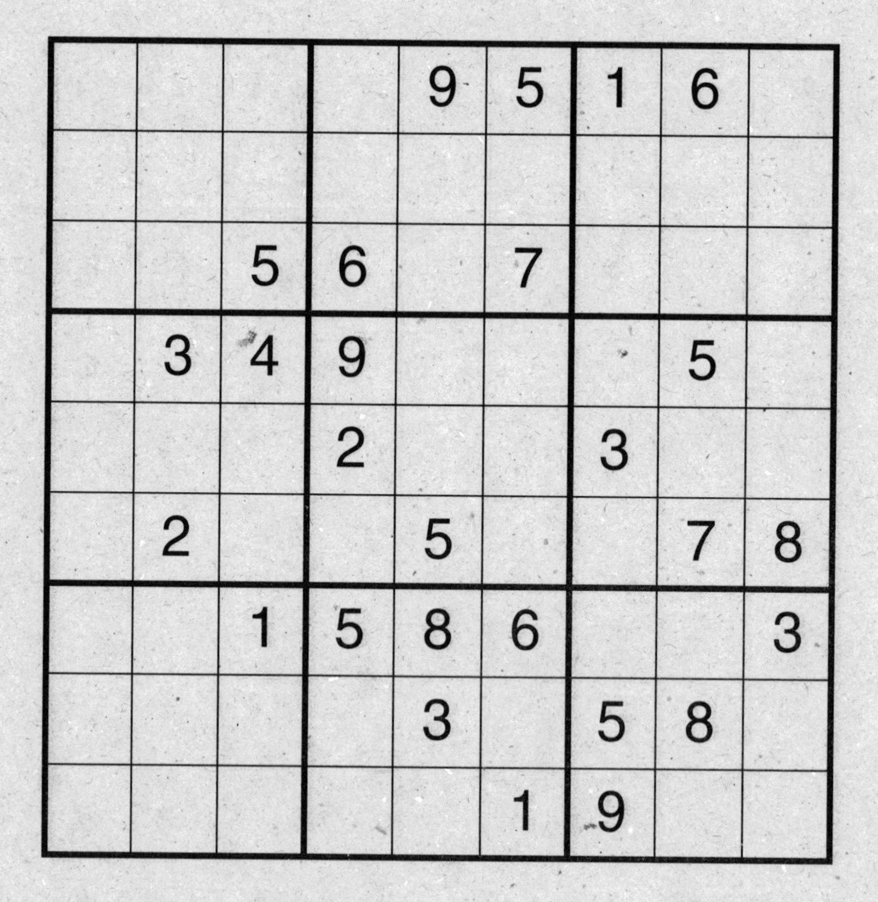

				9	5	1	6	
		5	6		7			
	3	4	9				5	
			2			3		
	2			5			7	8
		1	5	8	6			3
				3		5	8	
					1	9		

Medium SUDOKU

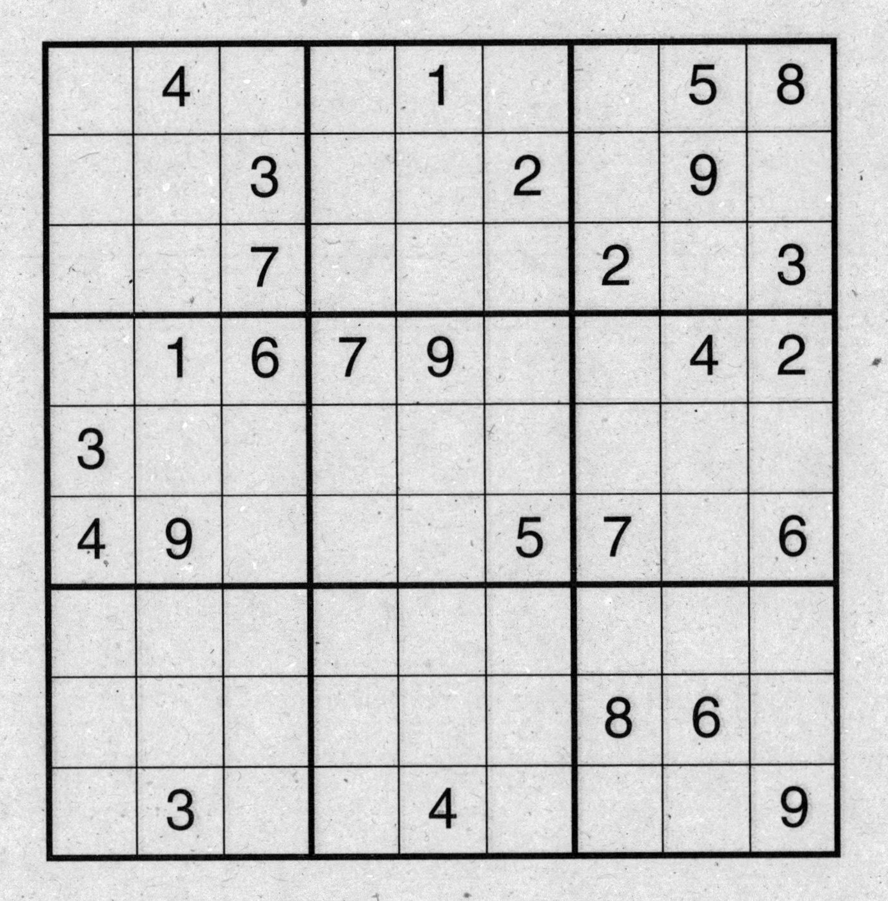

	4			1			5	8
		3			2		9	
		7				2		3
	1	6	7	9			4	2
3								
4	9				5	7		6
						8	6	
	3			4				9

Medium SUDOKU

					6			2
		6					4	7
			1		2		6	9
		8	9		5		7	
	9	3			8		5	
5			7				1	
			5					3
8		2	3		7			
	5							

Medium SUDOKU

1	9		4	8	6			
7								
	6	3	1	5		8		
			7	1		2		
					5			3
			3			5		
				3		9		8
			6		2		1	7
2			9					

Medium SUDOKU

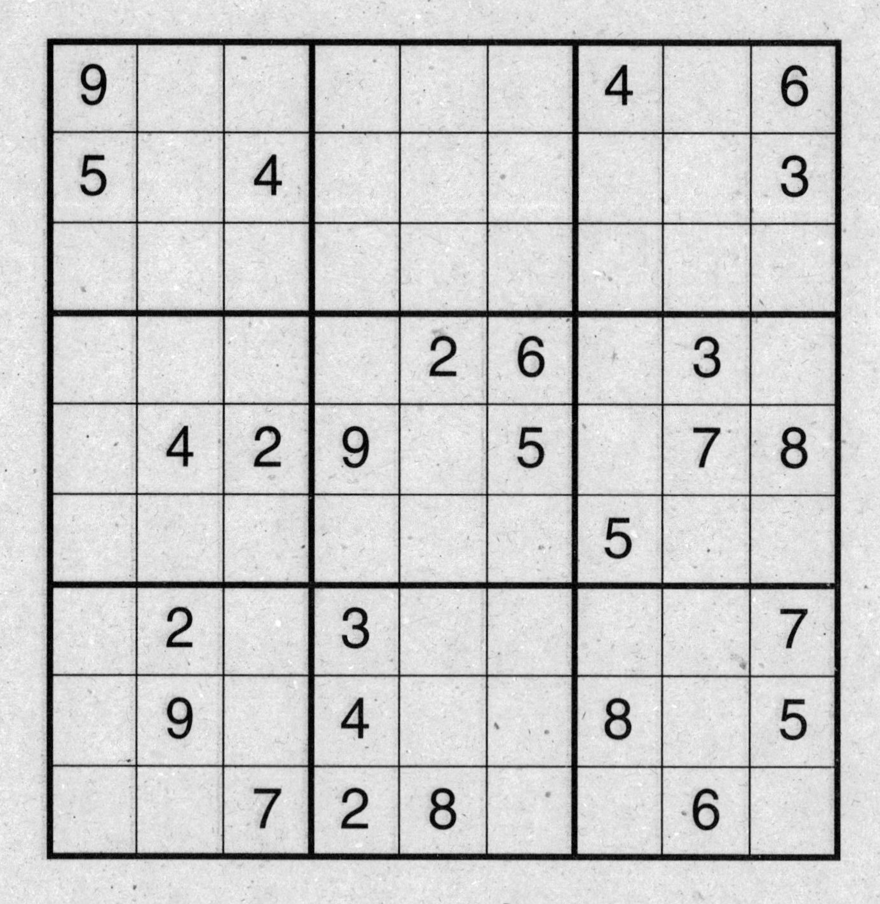

9						4		6
5		4						3
				2	6		3	
	4	2	9		5		7	8
						5		
	2		3					7
	9		4			8		5
		7	2	8			6	

Medium SUDOKU

	4				5	6	8	
		6						3
		2		3	8		5	
	9			7	2	5	6	
3			5			9		
		7		1		8		
						1	9	
			2	6	1			
							7	

Medium SUDOKU

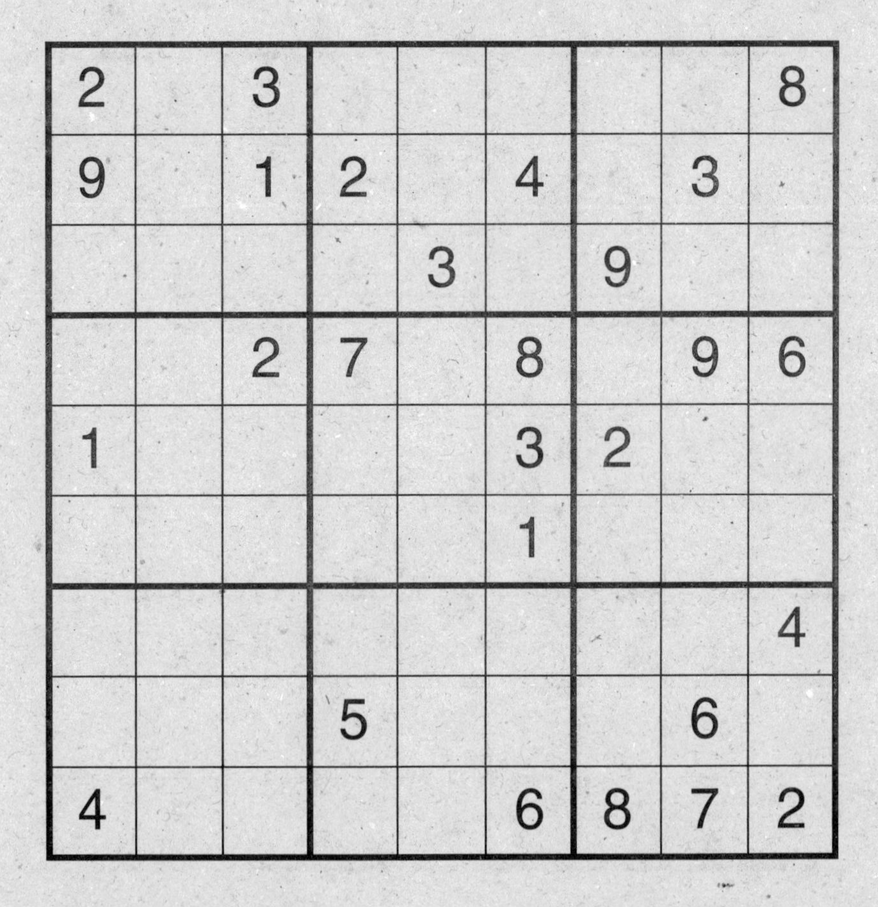

2		3						8
9		1	2		4		3	
				3		9		
		2	7		8		9	6
1					3	2		
					1			
								4
			5				6	
4					6	8	7	2

Medium SUDOKU

	5					8		
		4		9	2	1		
9		1					4	
			1					
	4		7	8		3		
					3			
2		3	6					8
			9			7		6
6		9	5		8		3	

Medium SUDOKU

		5	3	7		6		
	9			8	2			
	3				9	5		
	2	1					7	
				5		2		1
		7		4			3	
		2				3		
							6	7
		3	1			9	5	

Medium SUDOKU

	1							
		6		3	8		1	
4		5	2				6	
1	9		7				5	8
		7	4		5			9
					3			1
	2		8	5				
	4				7			
	3							7

Medium SUDOKU

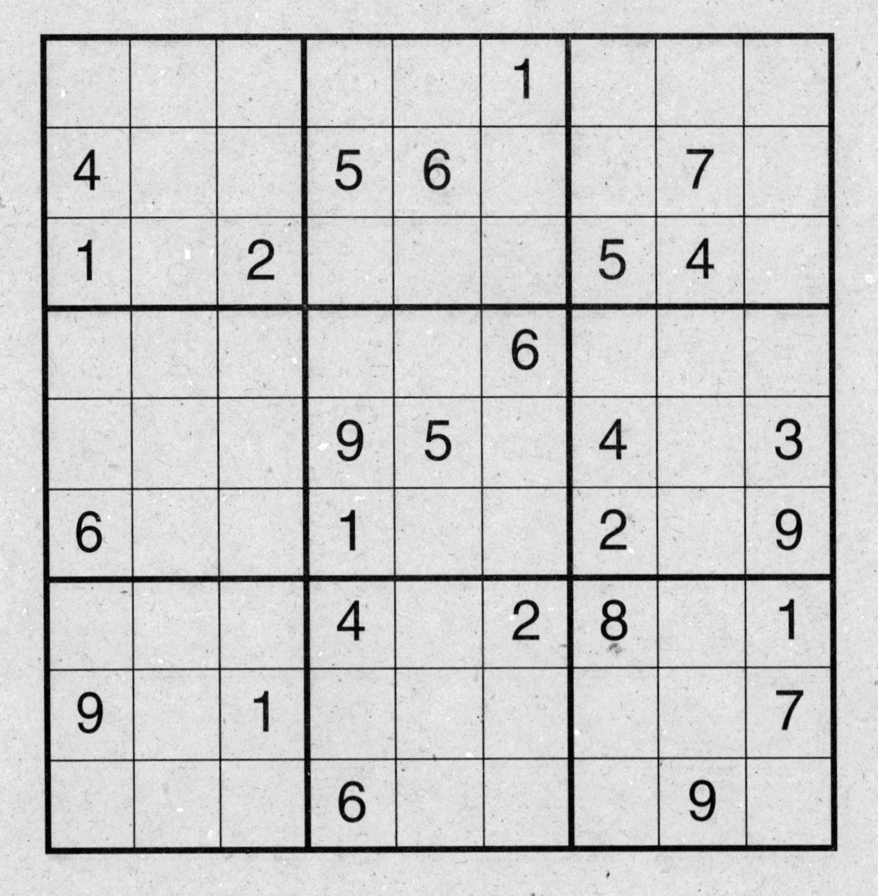

					1			
4			5	6			7	
1		2				5	4	
					6			
			9	5		4		3
6			1			2		9
			4		2	8		1
9		1						7
			6				9	

Medium SUDOKU

		6	2	3	7		8	
5		8			4	6	3	
					6		1	2
						4	9	
		3	1					
	5					2		
	4	9						
	6			9	3			
1		2			5			

Medium SUDOKU

	4			1	5			
8	5	7	2		6		3	
9			8					
						6		
5	6							
2			5					
		4					2	7
					8	3	6	
	8		3		1		9	4

Medium SUDOKU

					2			8
6		4	9	8		2		1
8			4					9
	9		7					4
7	5			9			3	
		6			3		1	
	6	5						
		8	1		7			5

Medium SUDOKU

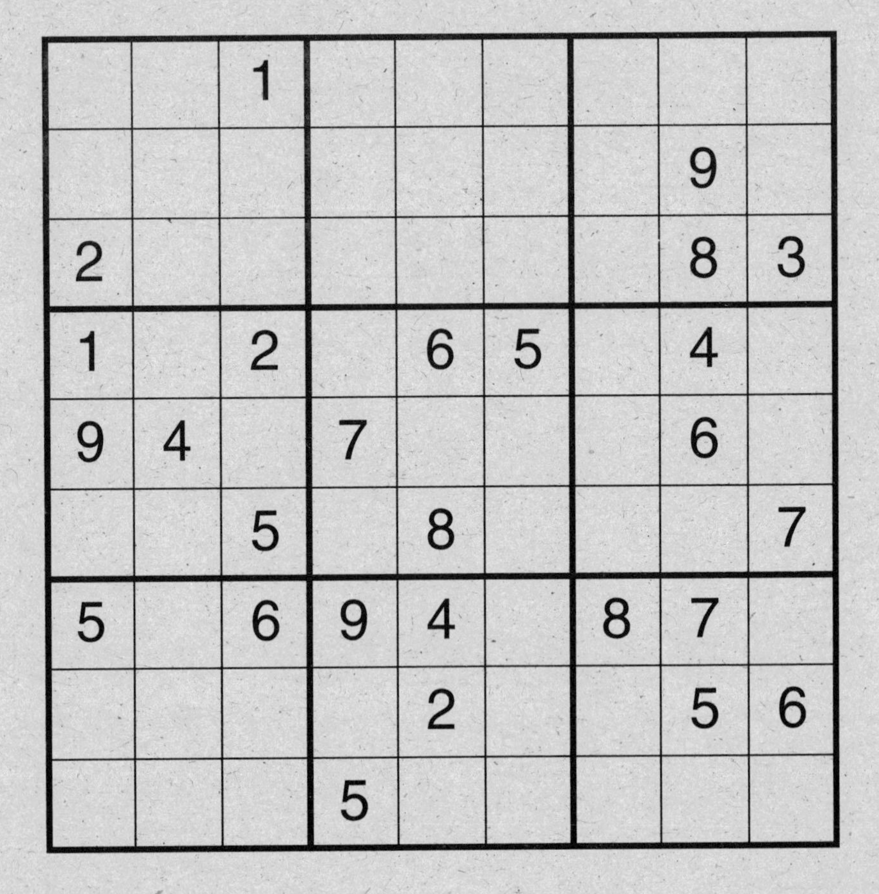

Medium SUDOKU

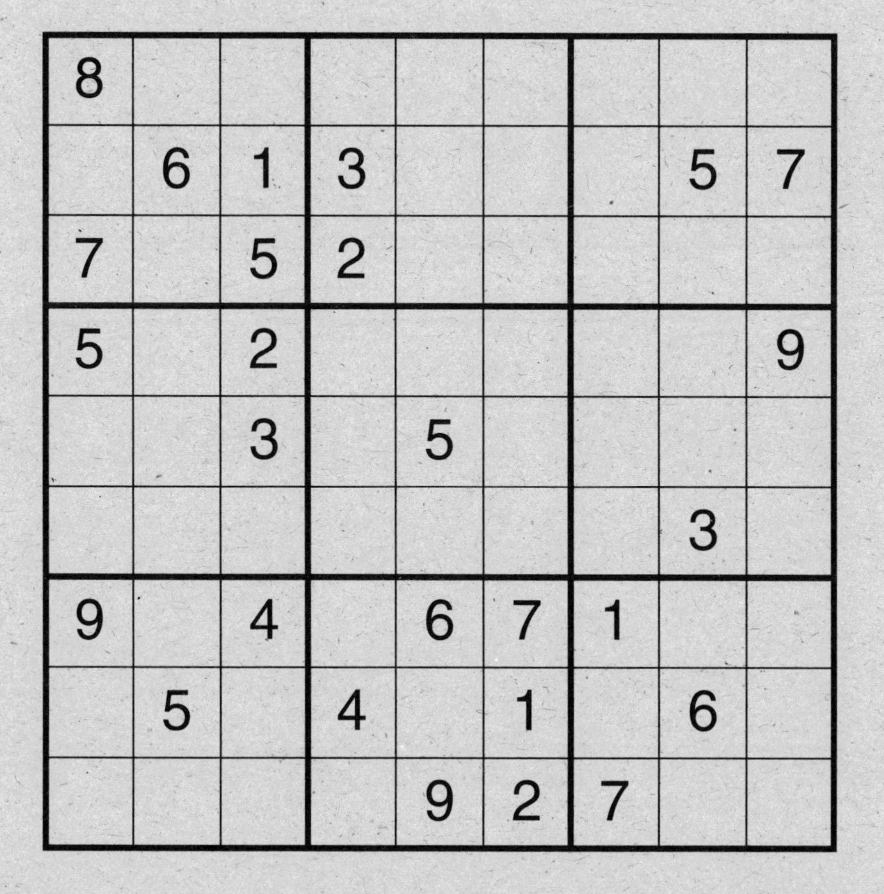

8								
	6	1	3				5	7
7		5	2					
5		2						9
		3		5				
							3	
9		4		6	7	1		
	5		4		1		6	
				9	2	7		

		7						
9	5		8			7	2	
		3		7		9		5
3			5	2			7	
		4		8			9	
2				4		5		8
4				5			8	
				3				4
						6		

Medium SUDOKU

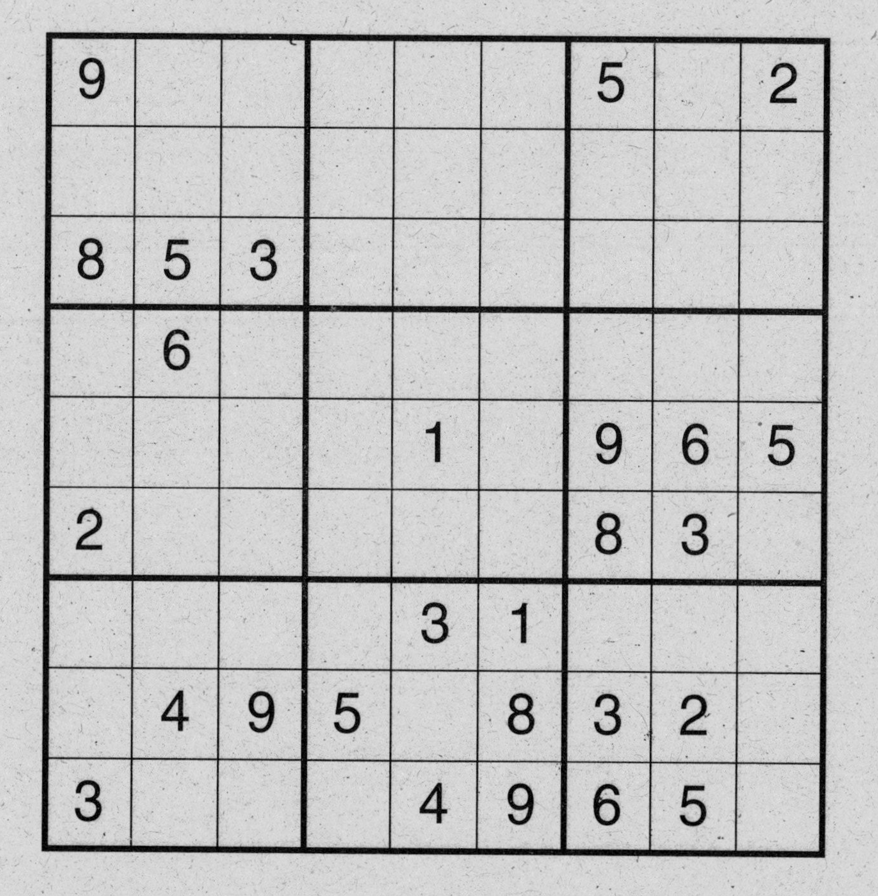

9						5		2
8	5	3						
	6							
				1		9	6	5
2						8	3	
				3	1			
	4	9	5		8	3	2	
3				4	9	6	5	

Medium SUDOKU

	5			7			3	
9			5					
8		4		1	6			
1		5	6					
			8	3	9		5	
	9							
		8			3	1	2	
2				6		5		
		9		8		6		

Medium SUDOKU

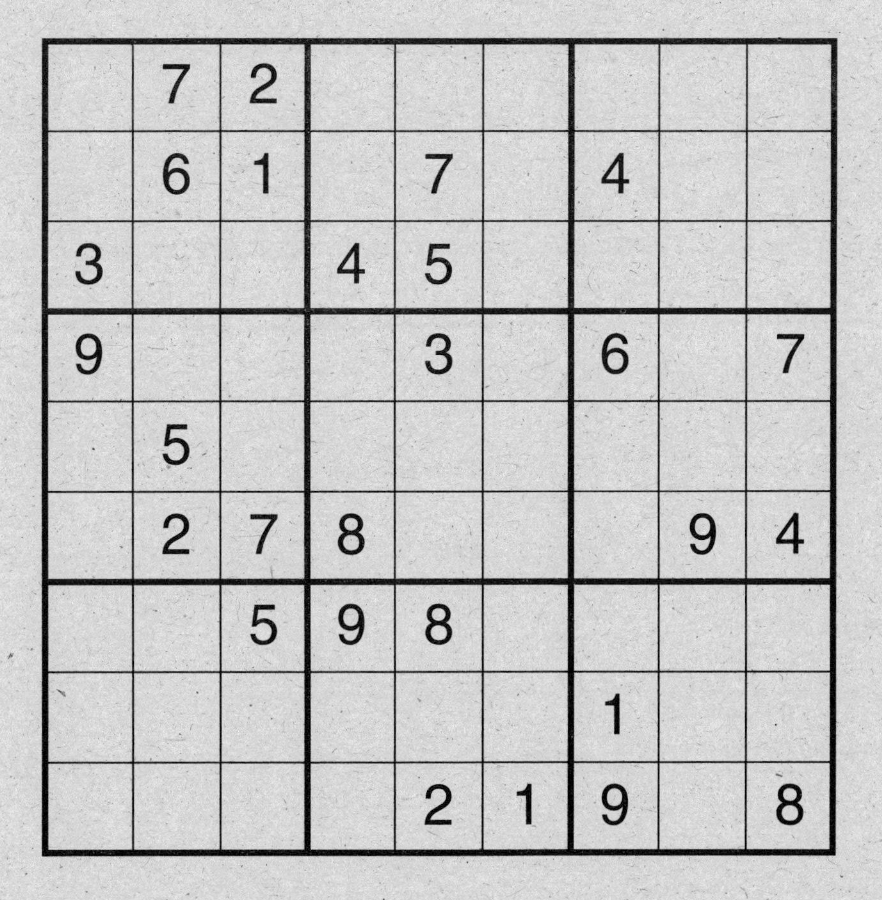

	7	2						
	6	1		7		4		
3			4	5				
9				3		6		7
	5							
	2	7	8				9	4
		5	9	8				
						1		
				2	1	9		8

Medium SUDOKU

	9				8		3	5
	4			1				
2			3				8	
			7	2				
	1							
				3	4			
	7	2	6					3
6	3		9	4			2	
4		9					6	8

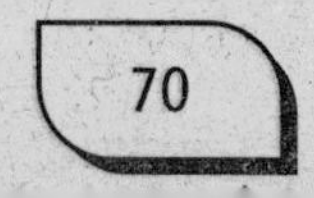

Hard SUDOKU

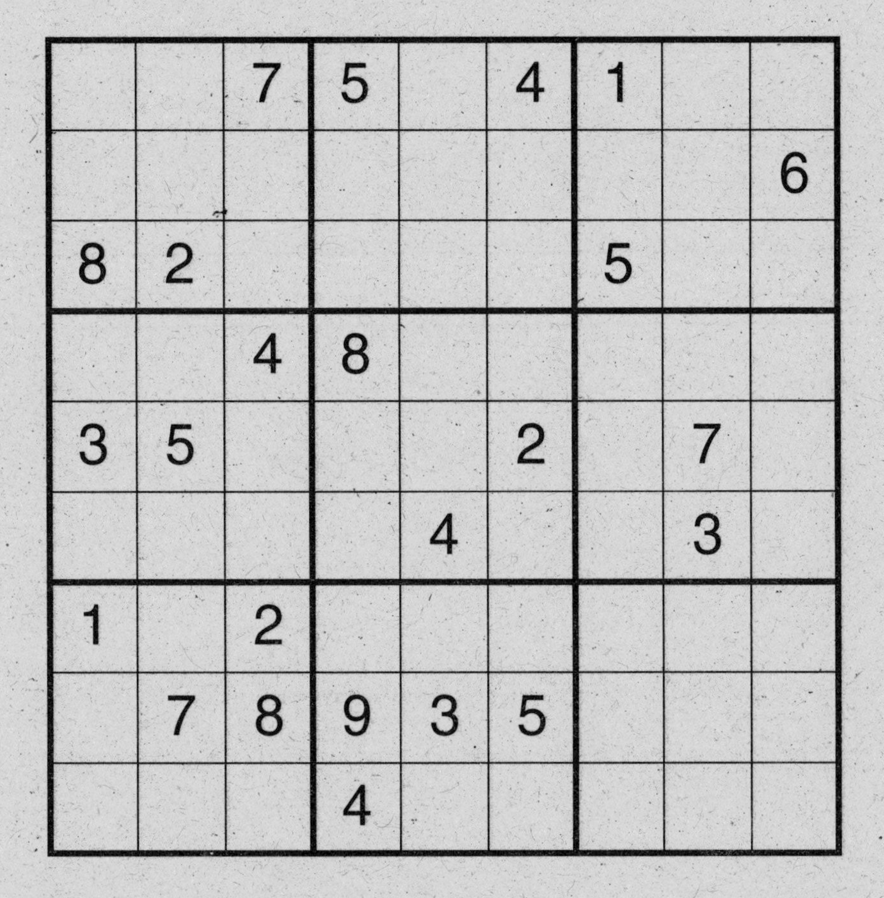

		7	5		4	1		
								6
8	2					5		
		4	8					
3	5				2		7	
				4			3	
1		2						
	7	8	9	3	5			
			4					

Hard SUDOKU

		7	9				8	
								3
	2			1				
8			4					
		4	3		2		6	
2		5						1
4		8	6	3		5		
6	9				7	4		

Hard SUDOKU

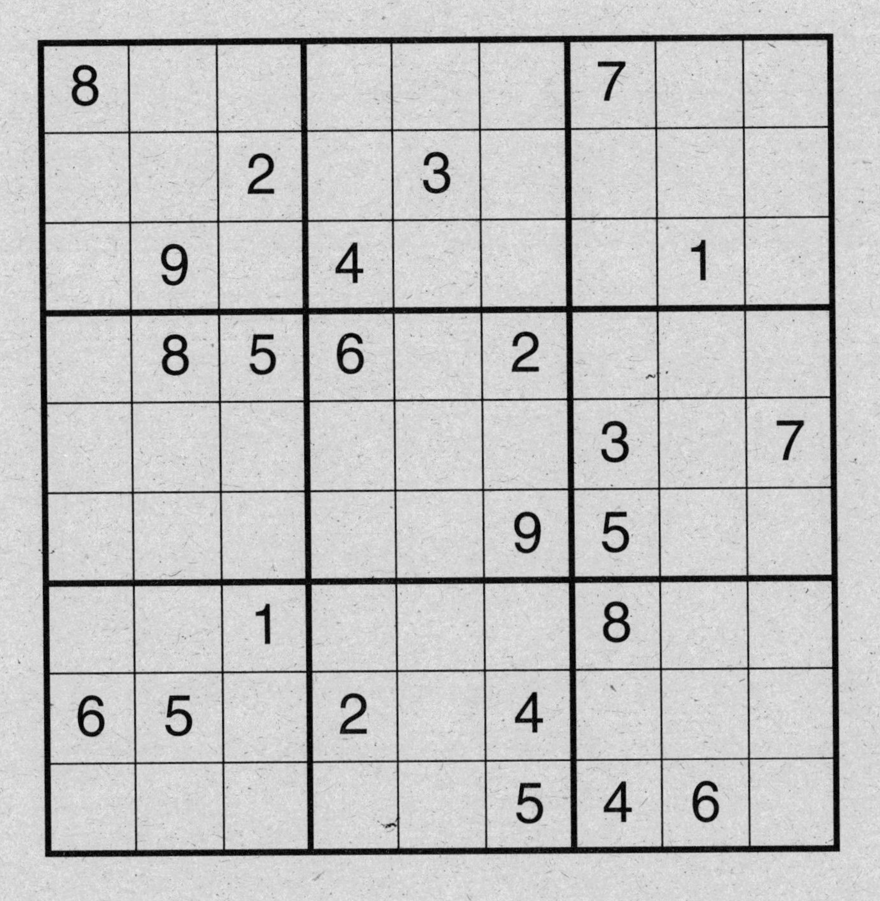

8						7		
		2		3				
	9		4				1	
	8	5	6		2			
						3		7
					9	5		
		1				8		
6	5		2		4			
					5	4	6	

Hard SUDOKU

8			9					
		3		6			8	
4	1		5				6	
		2		3		5		
1					6			2
					9	7		3
		7	4		1		2	
					2	4		

Hard SUDOKU

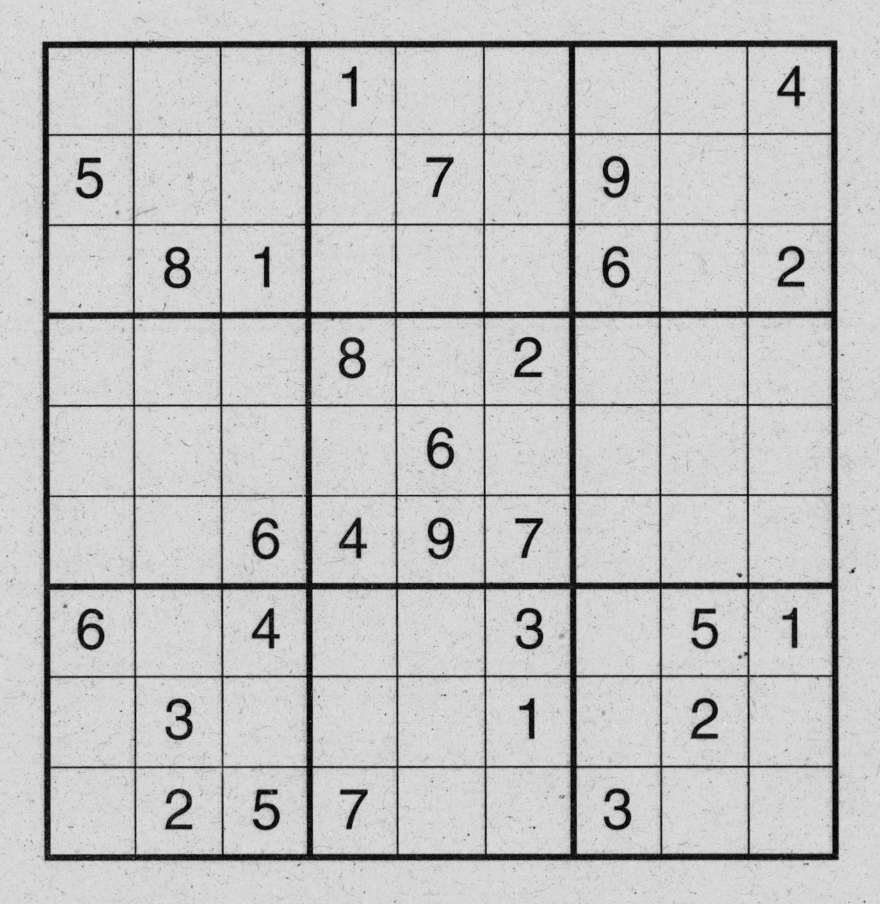

			1					4
5				7		9		
	8	1				6		2
			8		2			
				6				
		6	4	9	7			
6		4			3		5	1
	3				1		2	
	2	5	7			3		

Hard SUDOKU

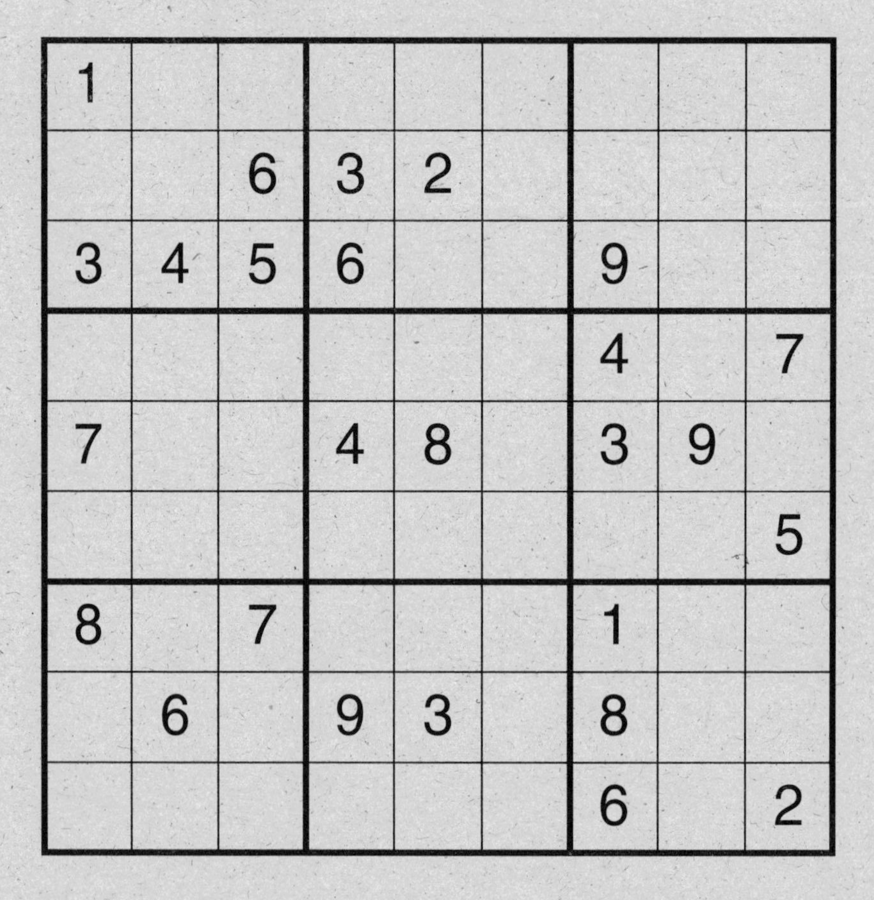

1								
		6	3	2				
3	4	5	6			9		
						4		7
7			4	8		3	9	
								5
8		7				1		
	6		9	3		8		
						6		2

Hard SUDOKU

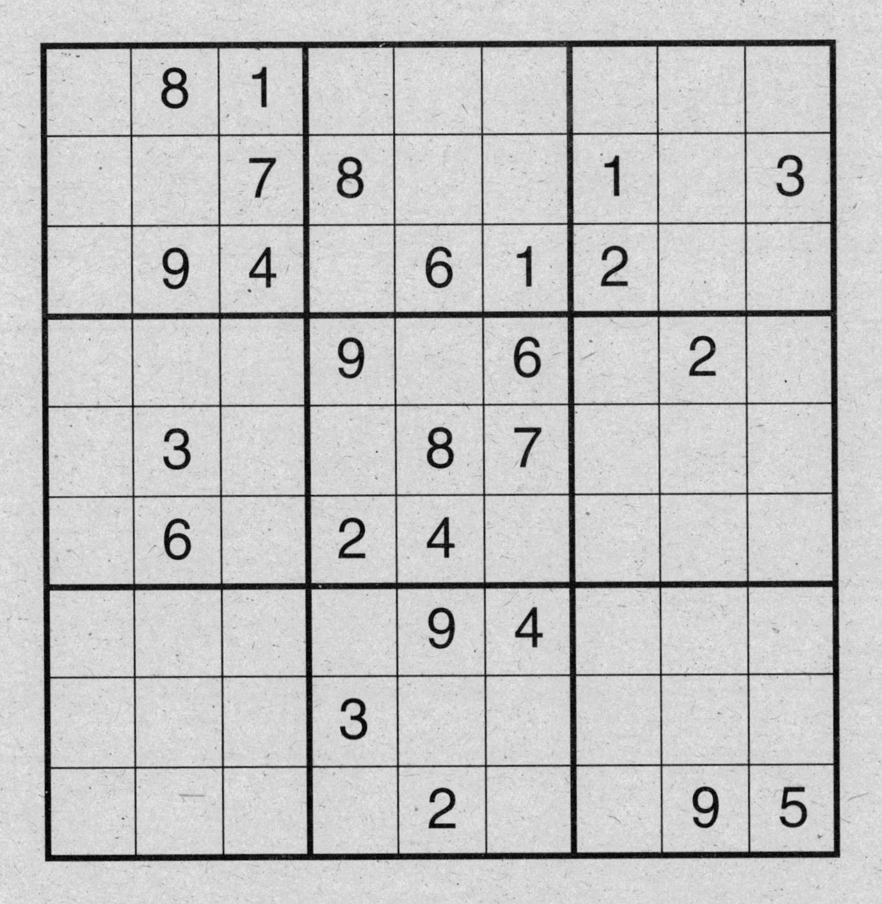

	8	1						
		7	8			1		3
	9	4		6	1	2		
			9		6		2	
	3			8	7			
	6		2	4				
				9	4			
			3					
				2			9	5

Hard SUDOKU

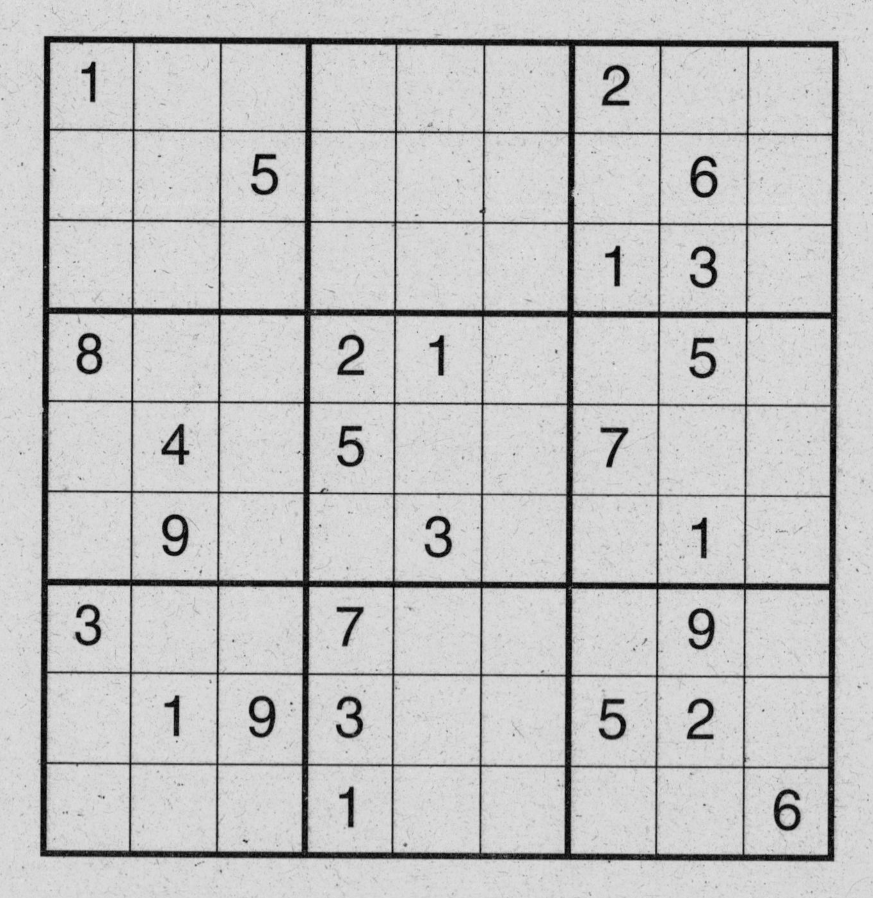

1						2		
		5					6	
						1	3	
8			2	1			5	
	4		5			7		
	9			3			1	
3			7				9	
	1	9	3			5	2	
			1					6

Hard SUDOKU

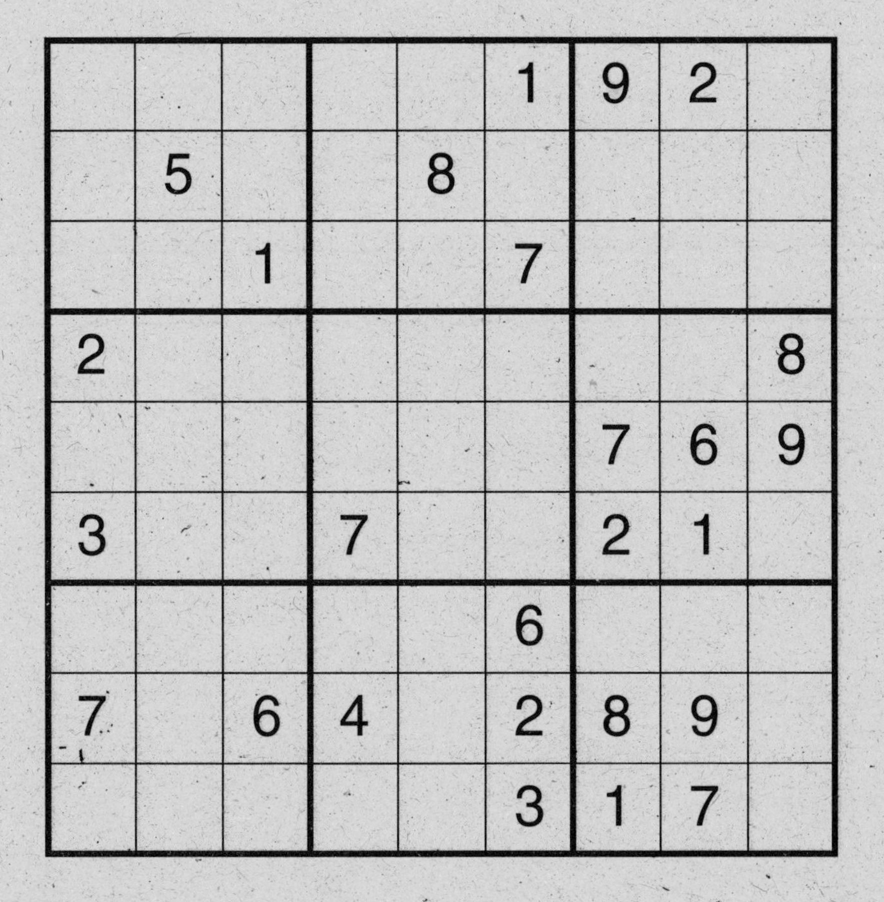

					1	9	2	
	5			8				
		1			7			
2								8
						7	6	9
3			7			2	1	
					6			
7		6	4		2	8	9	
					3	1	7	

Hard SUDOKU

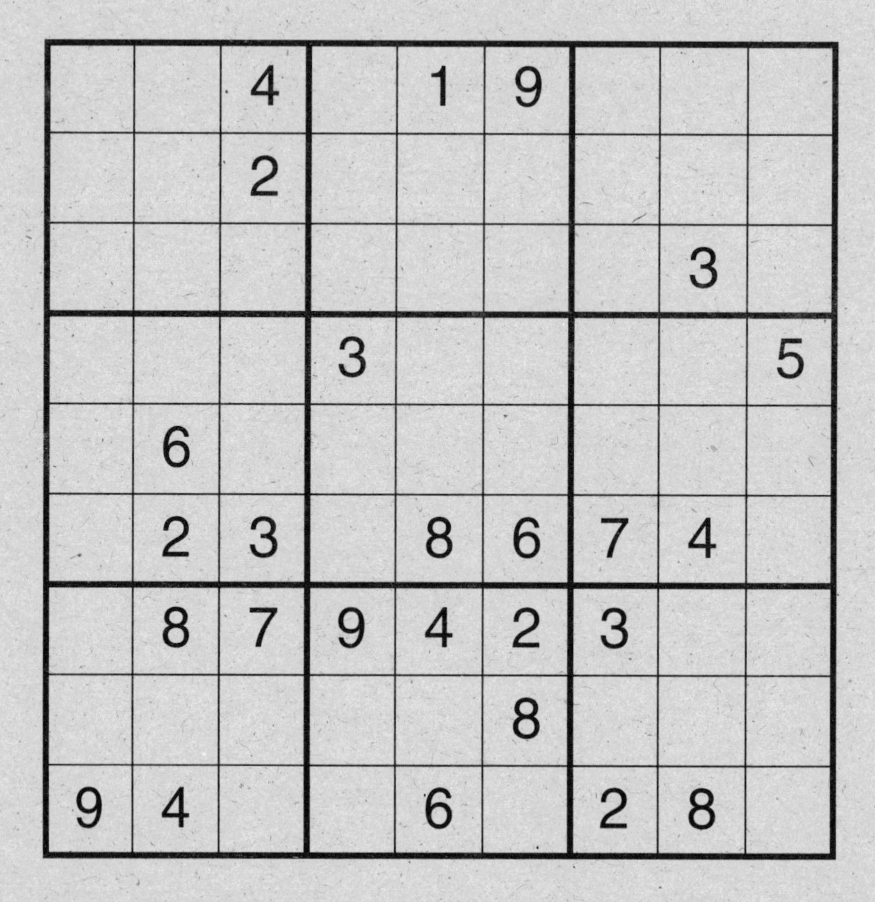

		4		1	9			
		2						
							3	
			3					5
	6							
	2	3		8	6	7	4	
	8	7	9	4	2	3		
					8			
9	4			6		2	8	

Hard SUDOKU

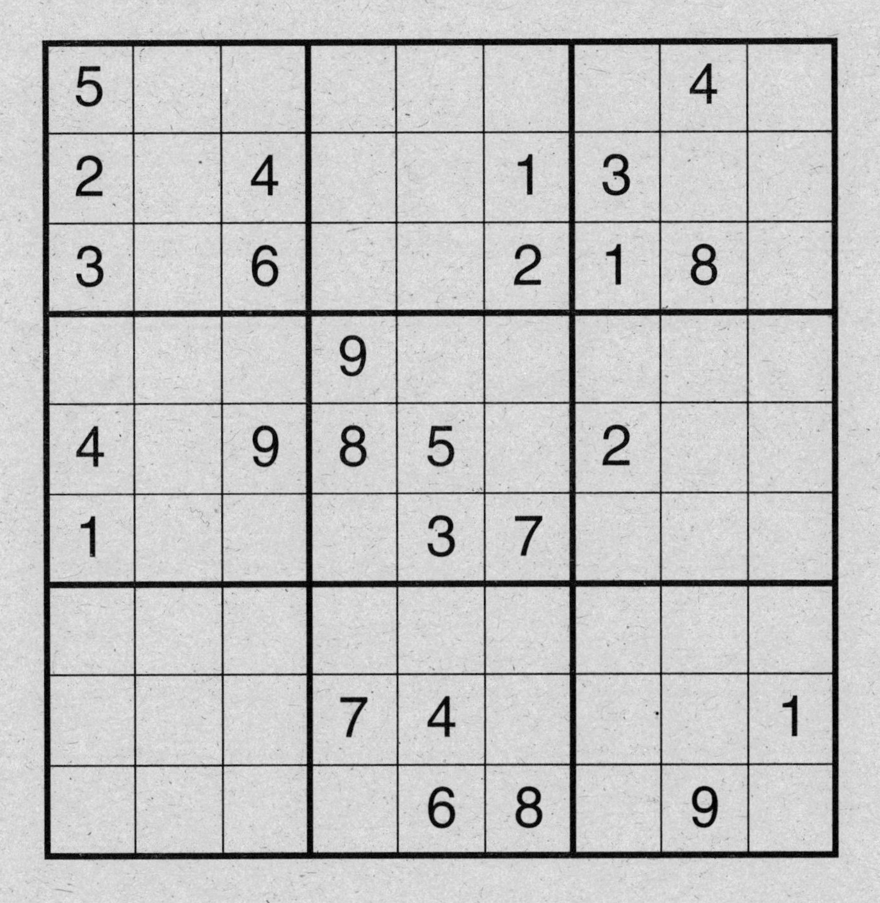

5							4	
2		4			1	3		
3		6			2	1	8	
			9					
4		9	8	5		2		
1				3	7			
			7	4				1
				6	8		9	

Hard SUDOKU

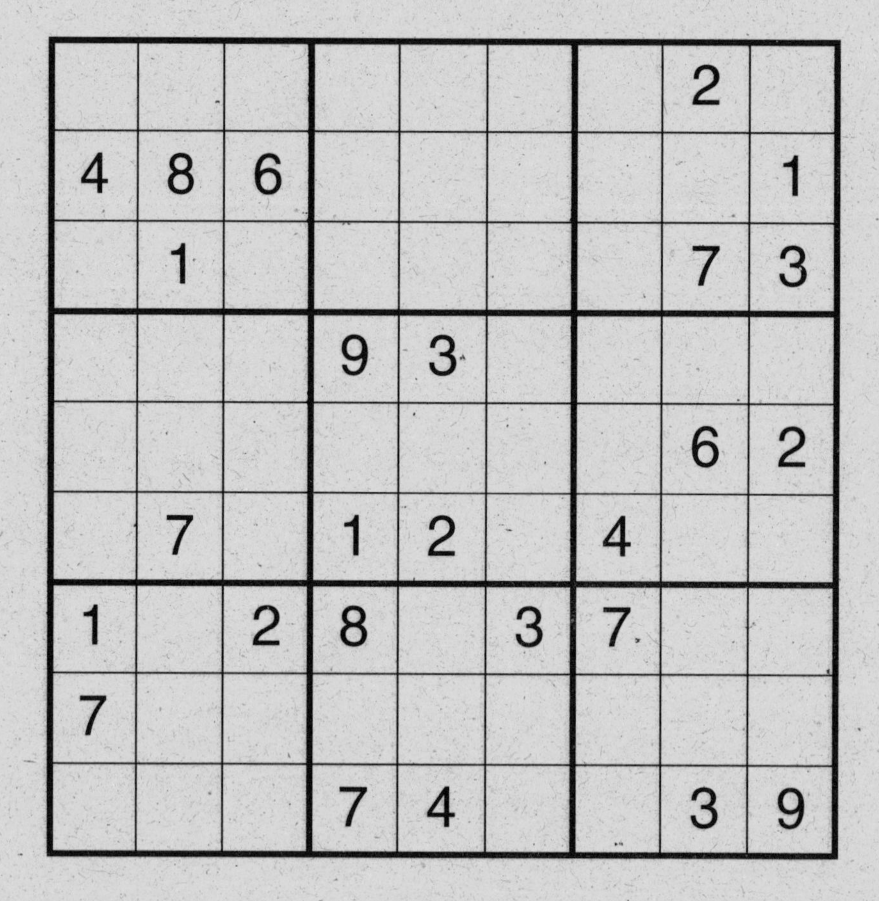

							2	
4	8	6						1
	1						7	3
			9	3				
							6	2
	7		1	2		4		
1		2	8		3	7		
7								
			7	4			3	9

Hard SUDOKU

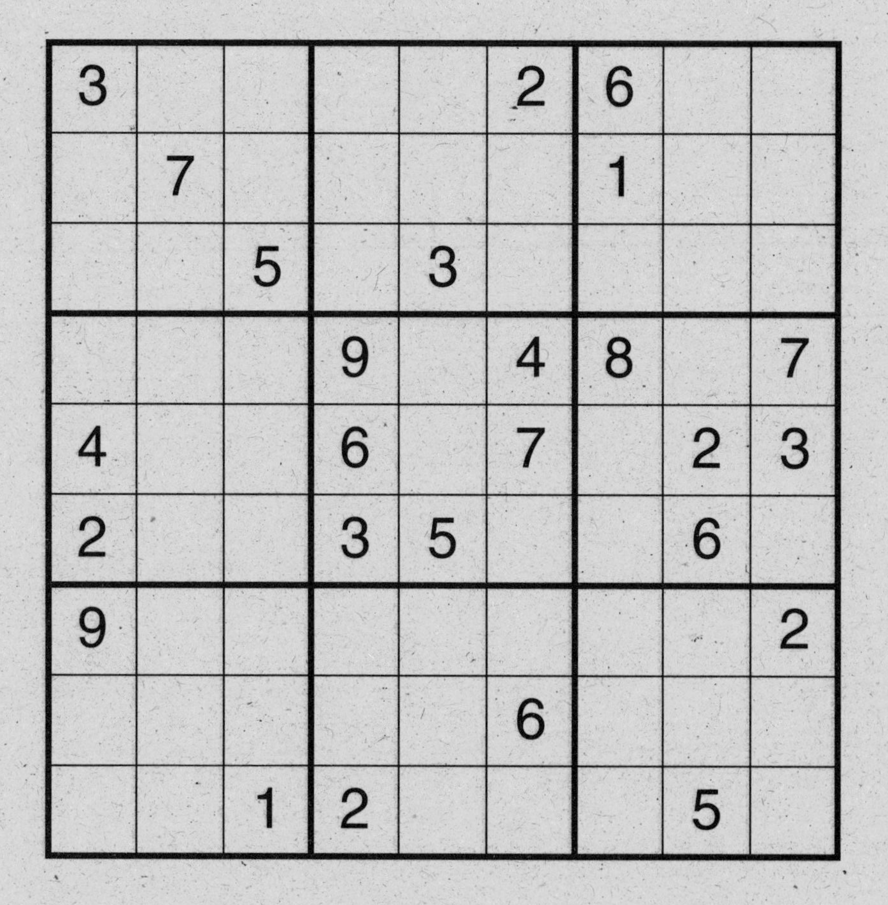

3					2	6		
	7					1		
		5		3				
			9		4	8		7
4			6		7		2	3
2			3	5			6	
9								2
					6			
		1	2				5	

Hard SUDOKU

		8	6			9	1	
			3		8			
4		5		9	1	8	2	
	7		2	6			9	
		9		4				
	2	1				6		
	1	2						
		6				5	4	

Hard SUDOKU

			9	1				5
		6	3	8	4	7		
		9	7					
6	1		5			9		
3			8				6	
				5				
8		3			9	2		
		7	1		3	8		

Hard SUDOKU

			2					
		7			8			6
			4					
	2	4	6	3		1		5
1		8						
7		5	8		9	3		4
		2				5		1
				9				
8			3		5		6	7

Hard SUDOKU

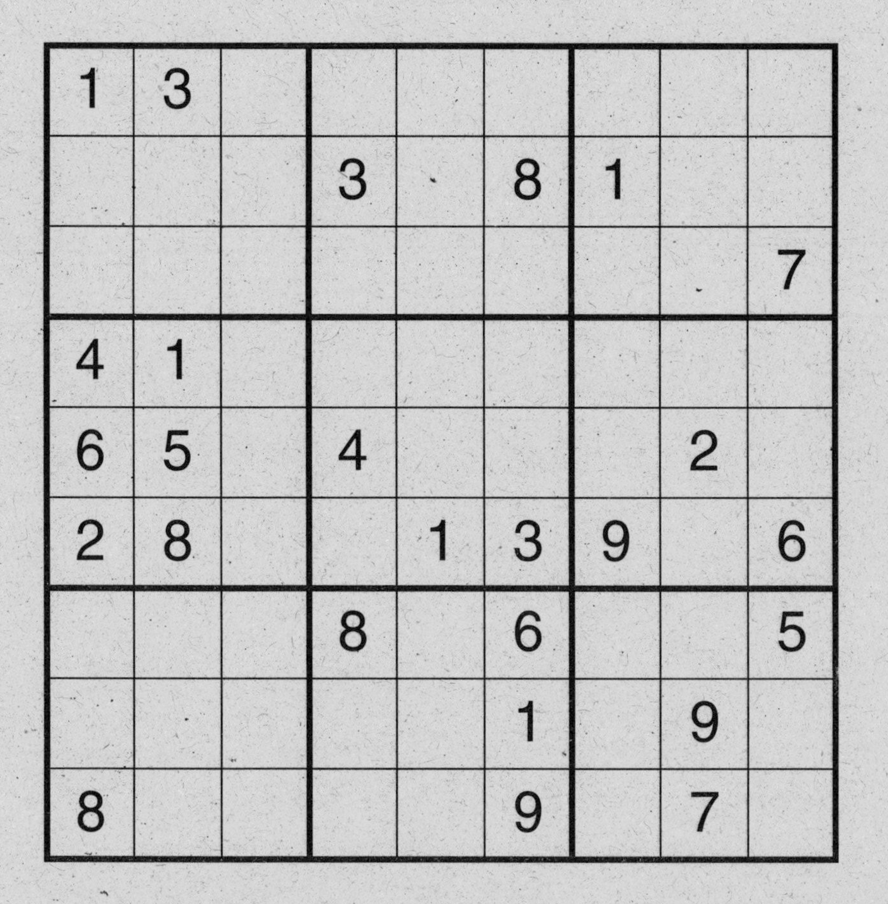

1	3							
			3		8	1		
								7
4	1							
6	5		4				2	
2	8			1	3	9		6
			8		6			5
					1		9	
8					9		7	

Hard SUDOKU

		3	8			7		5
9		5		3			8	
1		7					6	
					4	2	3	
			3	2				
	6			8		9		
			4		3			
					9	5	4	
		1	2					

Hard SUDOKU

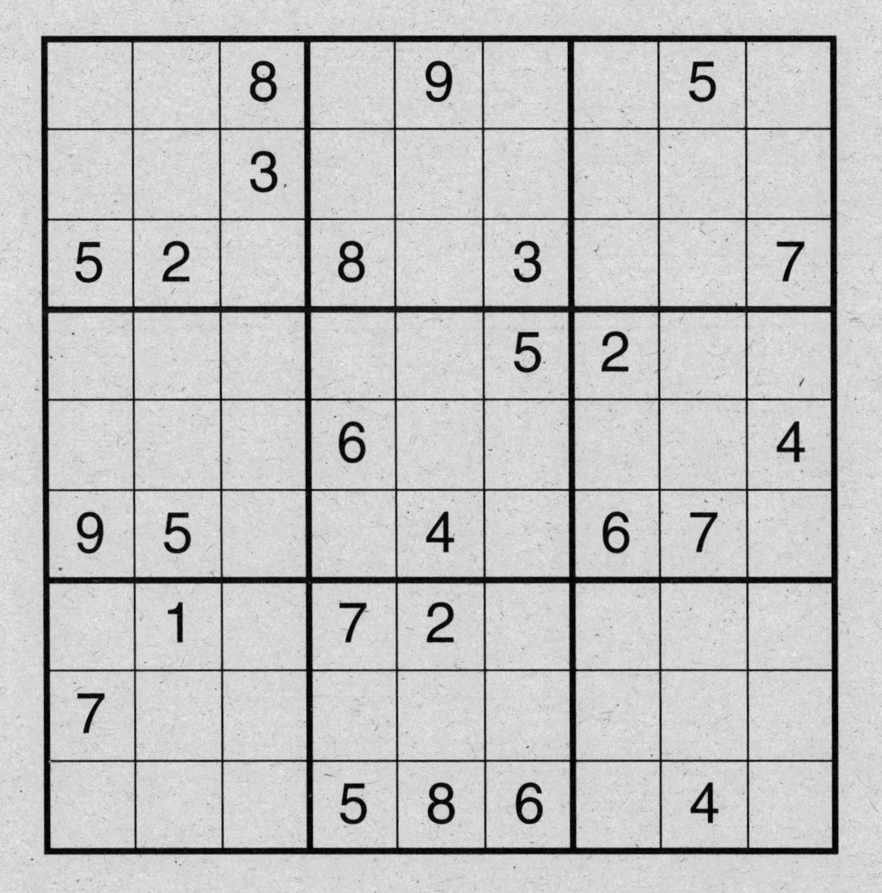

		8		9			5	
		3						
5	2		8		3			7
					5	2		
			6					4
9	5			4		6	7	
	1		7	2				
7								
			5	8	6		4	

Hard SUDOKU

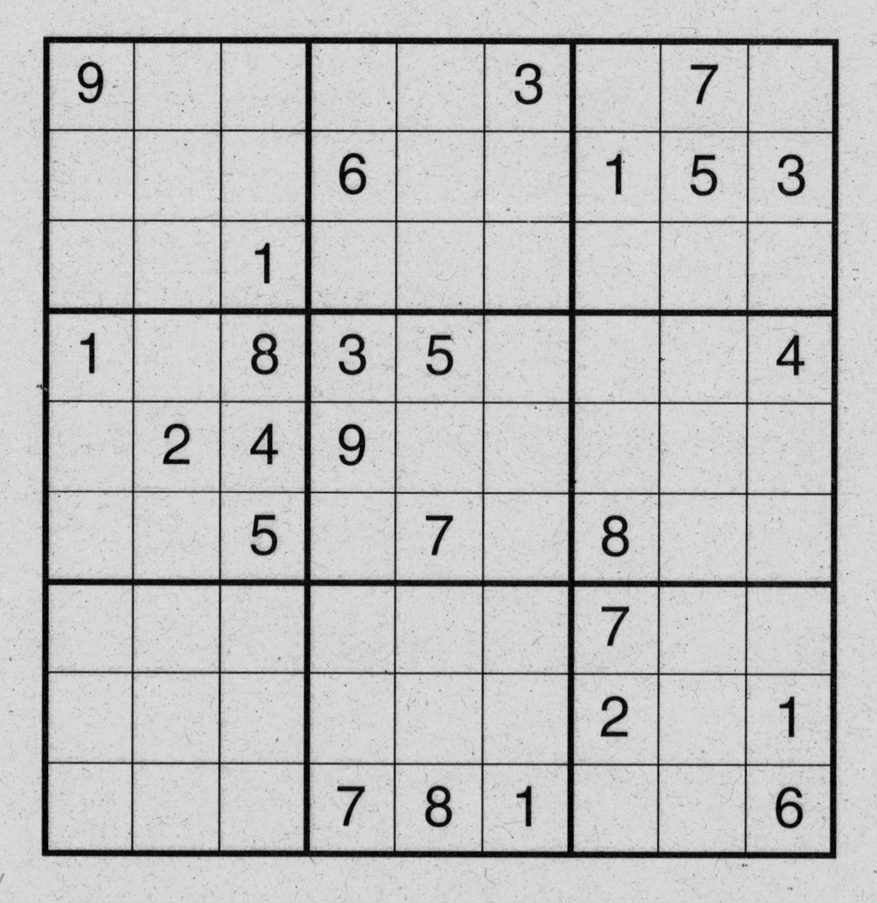

9					3		7	
			6			1	5	3
		1						
1		8	3	5				4
	2	4	9					
		5		7		8		
						7		
						2		1
			7	8	1			6

Hard SUDOKU

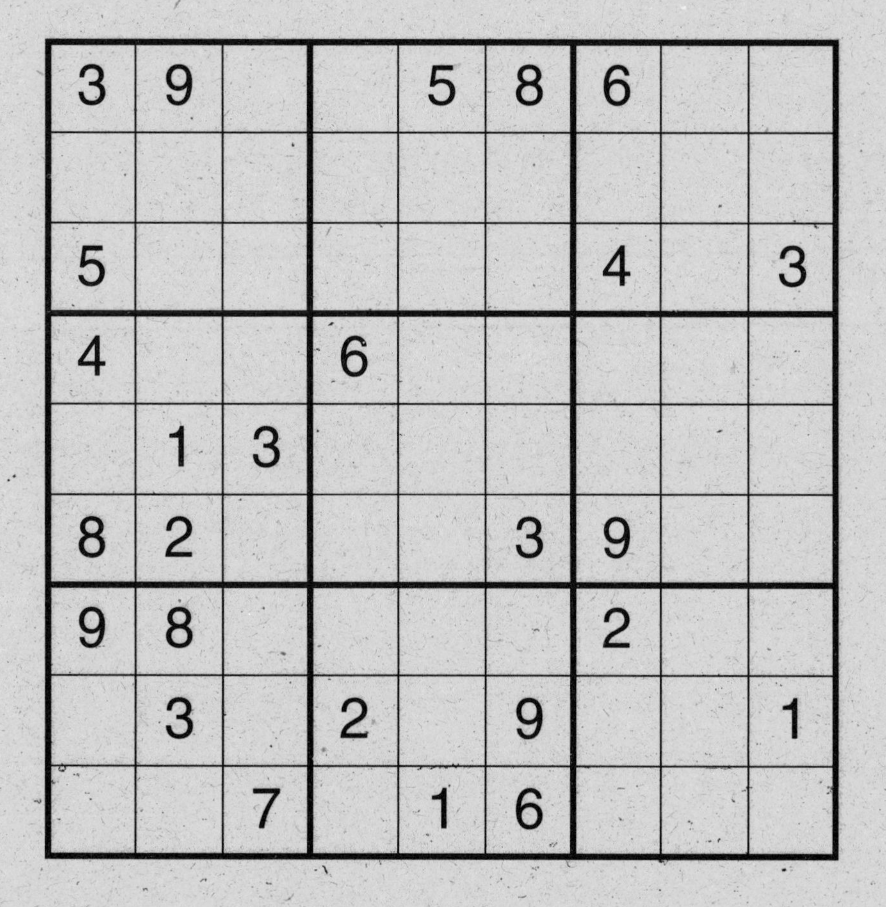

3	9			5	8	6		
5						4		3
4			6					
	1	3						
8	2				3	9		
9	8					2		
	3		2		9			1
		7		1	6			

Hard SUDOKU

	5			1			8	
9		6	5					1
					6			
					8			7
		3	6		7	4		
6			1			3		2
7	2						3	6
3	6	1	8		2			
		4						

Hard SUDOKU

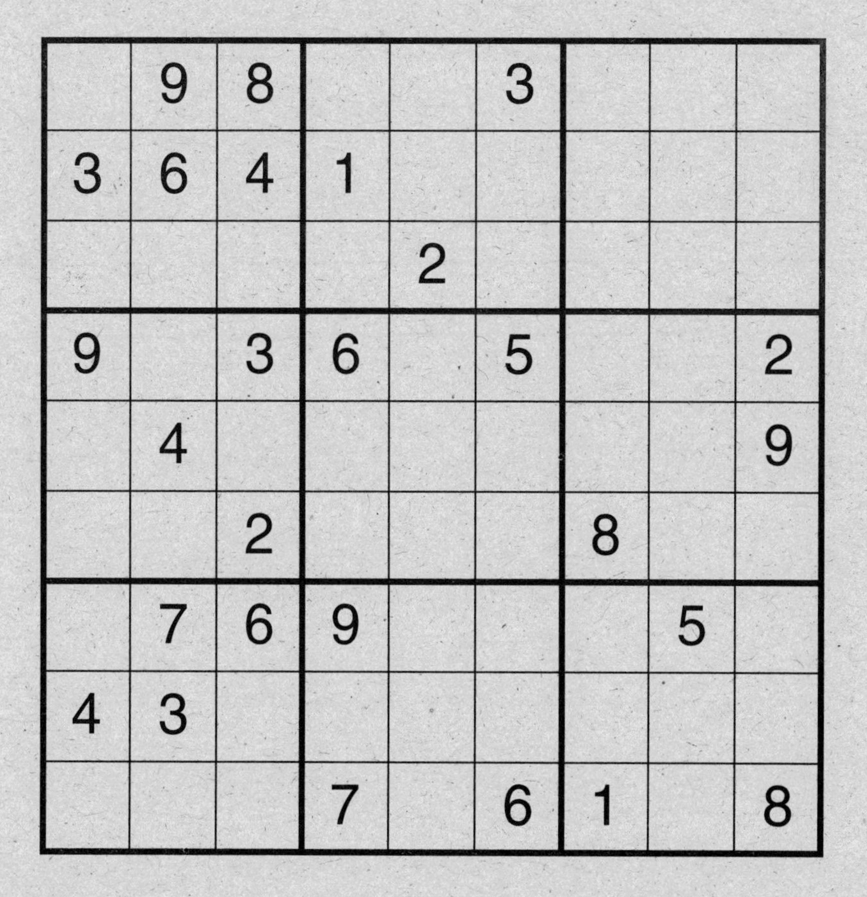

Hard SUDOKU

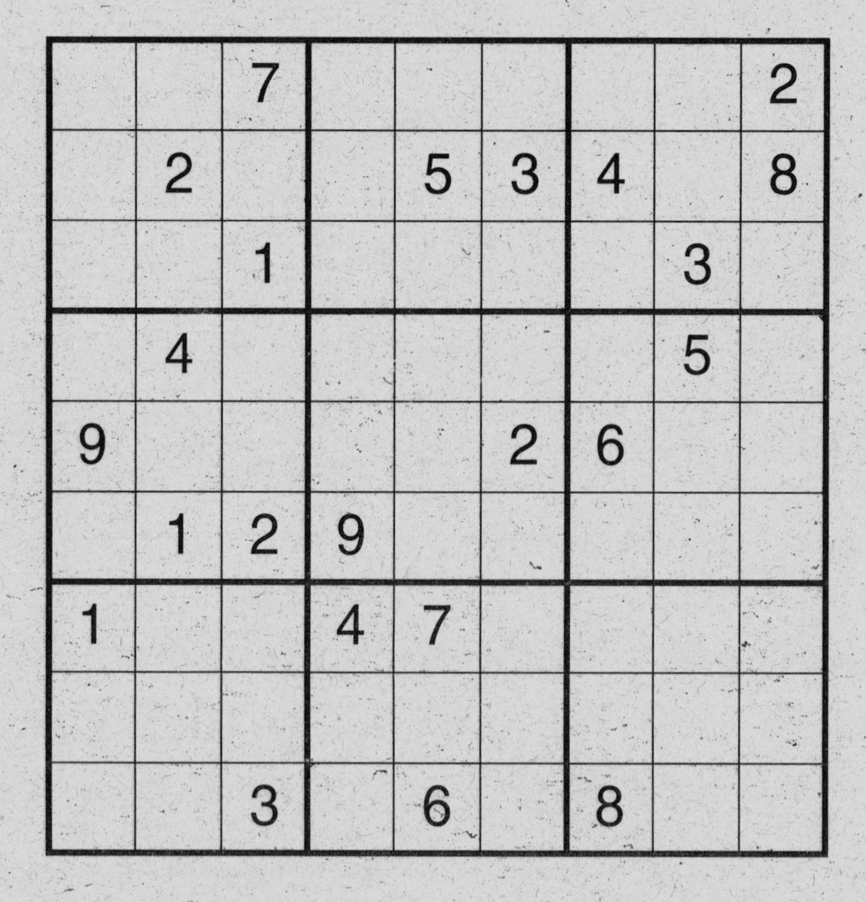

		7						2
	2			5	3	4		8
		1					3	
	4						5	
9					2	6		
	1	2	9					
1			4	7				
		3		6		8		

Hard SUDOKU

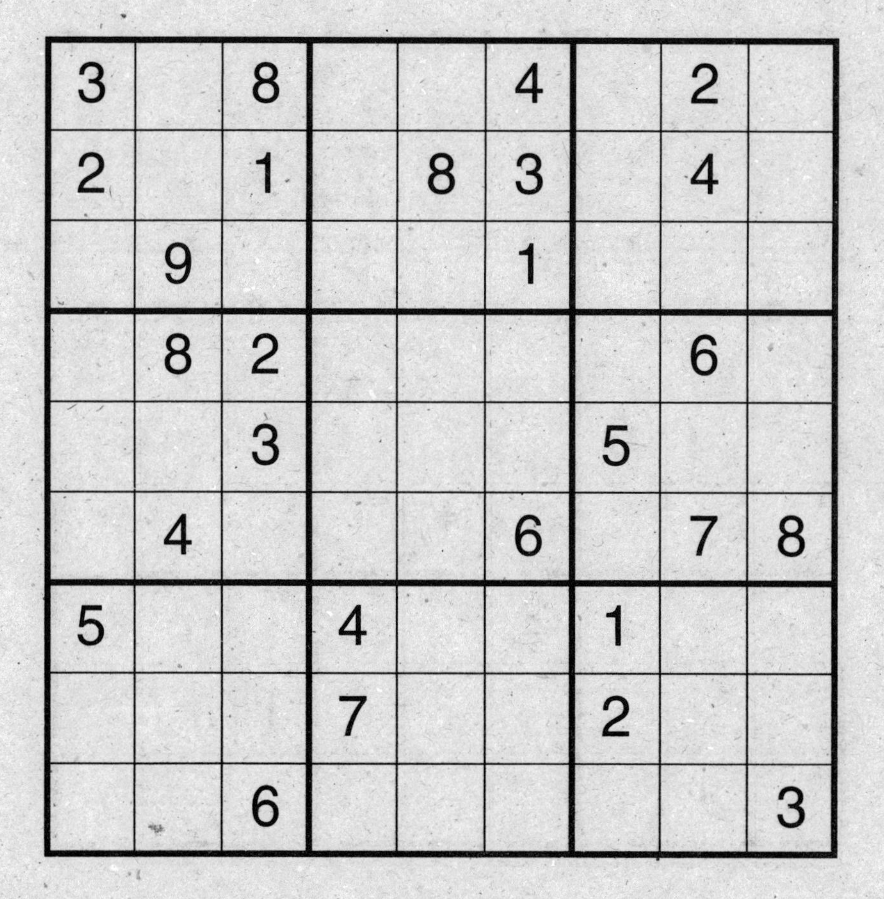

3		8			4		2	
2		1		8	3		4	
	9				1			
	8	2					6	
		3				5		
	4				6		7	8
5			4			1		
			7			2		
		6						3

Hard SUDOKU

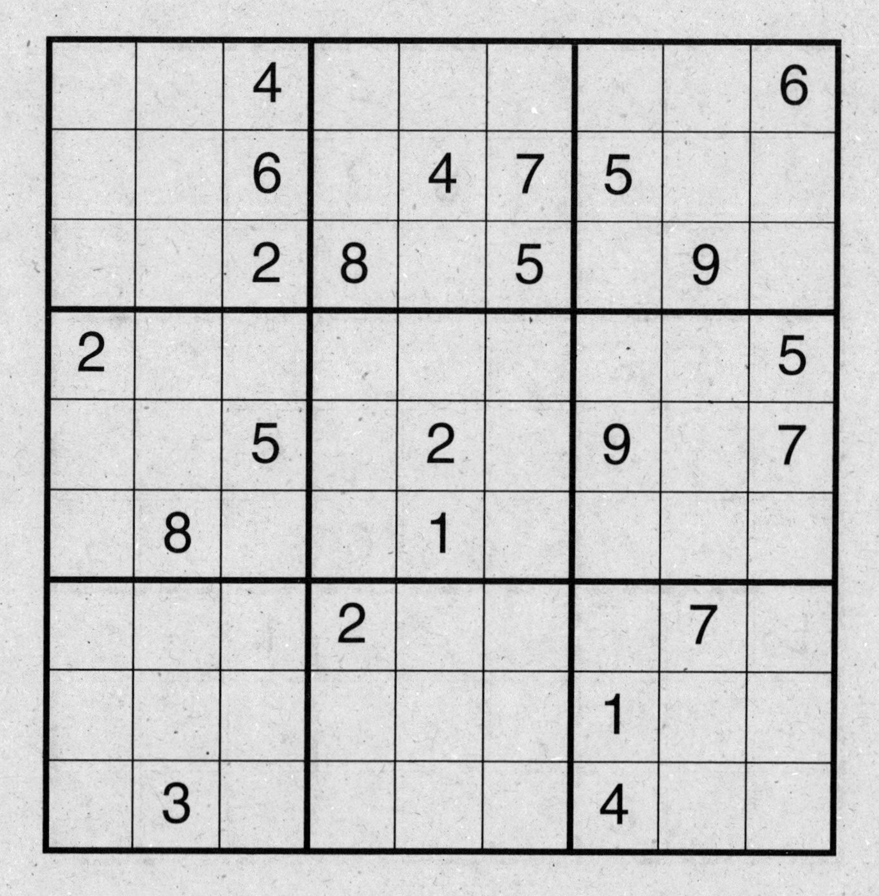

		4						6
		6		4	7	5		
		2	8		5		9	
2								5
		5		2		9		7
	8			1				
			2				7	
						1		
	3					4		

Hard SUDOKU

				8		7	6	
		2			7			9
					2	1		5
				6			7	
	1	3						
	8			3				
	3	9					5	
	5				4			
8	6		1					

Hard SUDOKU

			6			1	2	3
	2				5			
		6			1			
			5		3			9
	7			6		5	8	
5	4		9		2	8		
	3					7		
								1

Hard SUDOKU

2			6					
7				8	3			5
		6		4				9
	5					1		
			1			8		
	4							
3					7	5		
					4			7
	7			3			2	6

Hard SUDOKU

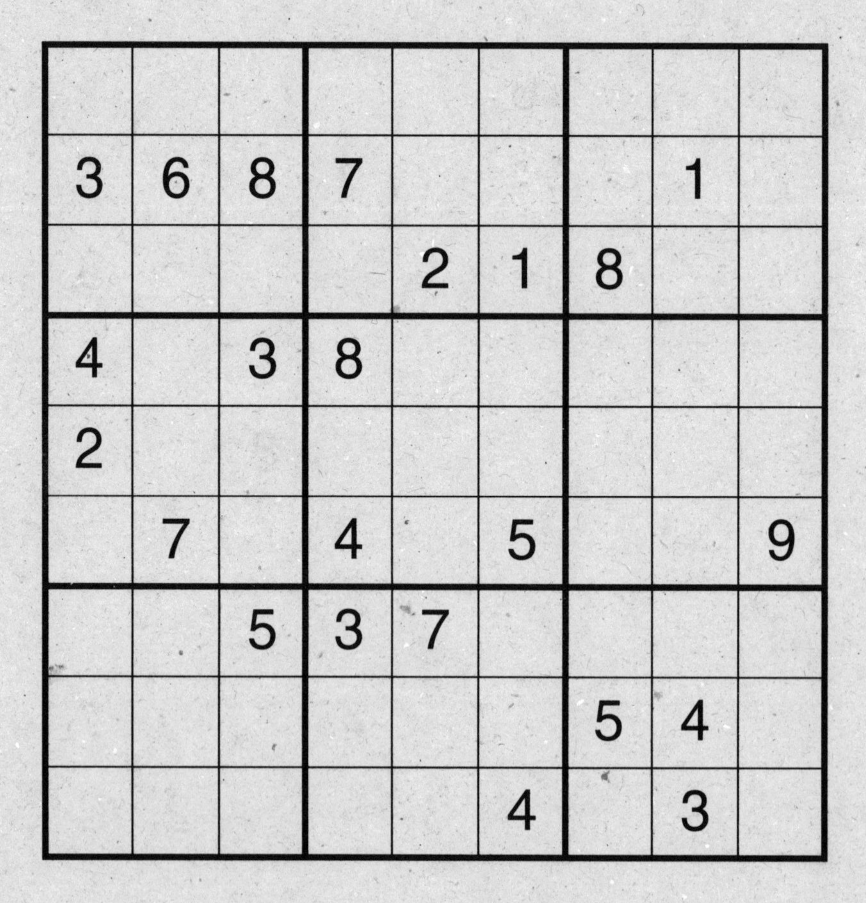

3	6	8	7				1	
				2	1	8		
4		3	8					
2								
	7		4		5			9
		5	3	7				
						5	4	
					4		3	

Hard SUDOKU

		1		9		4	3	
							1	
	2				5	9		
5		4						6
	9		6					
1		2					7	
9			2					
		8	1			3		
			4					1

Hard SUDOKU

			3	8				2
	5	2						6
		3	7			4		8
4	1				7			
					2			
								3
			9	6	3			
	4				8		2	
6							1	

Hard SUDOKU

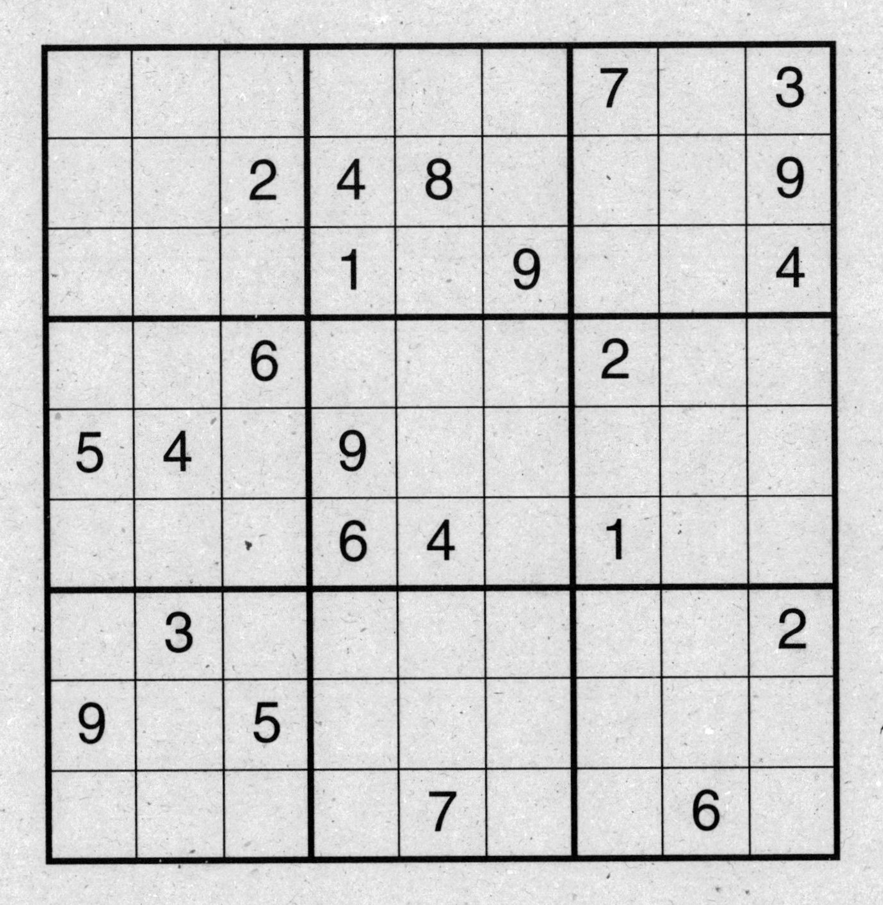

						7		3
		2	4	8				9
			1		9			4
		6				2		
5	4		9					
			6	4		1		
	3							2
9		5						
				7			6	

Hard SUDOKU

				7	1	6		
	4		3					5
						4		9
	3						2	
	1			3			5	
		2			8			
5		6	7				1	8
		8	2					
	7							

Hard SUDOKU

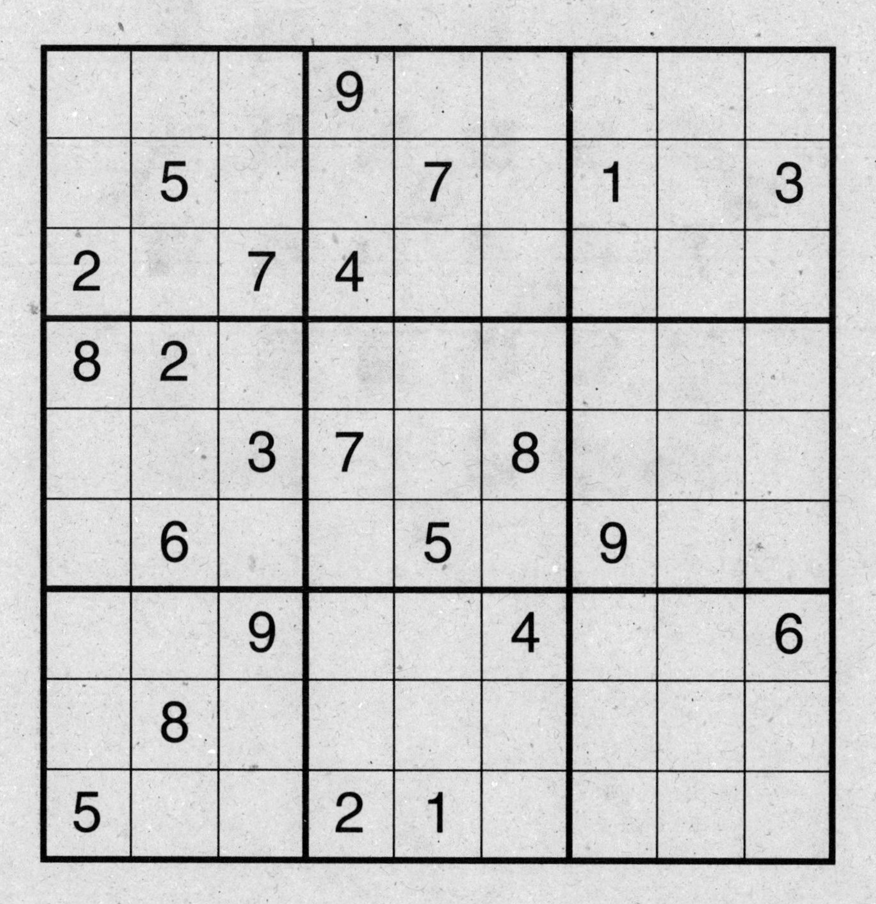

			9					
	5			7		1		3
2		7	4					
8	2							
		3	7		8			
	6			5		9		
		9			4			6
	8							
5			2	1				

Crosswords

Across

1 - Indigenous (6)

3 - Revolves (6)

7 - Removing particles (9)

9 - Firsthand (8)

10 - Smoke passage (4)

12 - Manners of walking (5)

13 - Protective coverings (5)

17 - Fourth Gospel (4)

18 - Confined (8)

20 - Fill again (9)

21 - Division of a group (6)

22 - Fortifying (6)

Down

1 - No one (6)

2 - Swiftness (8)

4 - Sound (4)

5 - Make soft (6)

6 - Closes (5)

7 - Assemble (9)

8 - Bird with yellow wing bar (9)

11 - Hotel-keeper (8)

14 - Walled inlets (6)

15 - Numerical scale (5)

16 - Border (6)

19 - Soup (anag) (4)

Crosswords

Across

1 - Capital of the Bahamas (6)

7 - Angel (8)

8 - Gang (3)

9 - Raised (6)

10 - Specks (4)

11 - Japanese fish dish (5)

13 - Radiant (7)

15 - Window above a door (7)

17 - Go away (5)

21 - Anchored float (4)

22 - Seldom (6)

23 - Male person (3)

24 - Passageway (8)

25 - Transmitter (6)

Down

1 - Female spirits (6)

2 - Swords (6)

3 - Supersede (5)

4 - Forced (7)

5 - Outbreak (8)

6 - Heed (6)

12 - Type of melon (8)

14 - Sadnesses (7)

16 - Russian monetary unit (6)

18 - Tallied (6)

19 - Complainer (6)

20 - Wears (5)

Crosswords

Across

1 - Foot support (7)

4 - Develops (5)

7 - Information (5)

8 - Late (7)

9 - Repudiate (4)

10 - Utilise (3)

11 - Monarch (4)

15 - One offs (9)

17 - Killed (4)

19 - Sail (3)

20 - Hilltop (4)

24 - Shaky (7)

25 - Numerical scale (5)

26 - Indoor game (5)

27 - Delivery men (7)

Down

1 - Supported (5)

2 - Significances (7)

3 - Cut of beef (4)

4 - Give food to (4)

5 - Travels (5)

6 - Smiled contemptuously (7)

8 - Haze (9)

12 - Antelope (3)

13 - Light brown (3)

14 - Toured (7)

16 - Bondage (7)

18 - Organic compound (5)

21 - Pallid (5)

22 - Weds (anag) (4)

23 - Covers (4)

Crosswords

Across

1 - Lines of a poem (6)

7 - Consecrate (8)

8 - Flightless bird (3)

9 - Round object (6)

10 - Overly submissive (4)

11 - Fluoresceine (5)

13 - Have (7)

15 - Gather (7)

17 - Inert gas (5)

21 - Test (anag) (4)

22 - Compel (6)

23 - Label (3)

24 - Eg Rudolph (8)

25 - Guardian (6)

Down

1 - Case (6)

2 - Mistreats (6)

3 - Fools (5)

4 - Surround entirely (7)

5 - Fine perfume sprayer (8)

6 - Supplies (6)

12 - Alluring (8)

14 - Variety of pool (7)

16 - Vent (6)

18 - Segregated district (6)

19 - Candy (6)

20 - Sound loudly (5)

Crosswords

Across

1 - Priest (7)

4 - Breathes fast and hard (5)

7 - Word of farewell (5)

8 - Speaker (7)

9 - Close (4)

10 - Part of pen (3)

11 - English monk (4)

15 - Extirpate (9)

17 - Official language of Pakistan (4)

19 - Excavate (3)

20 - Predatory canine mammal (4)

24 - Movement to music (7)

25 - Original (5)

26 - Honoured ladies (5)

27 - Withstands (7)

Down

1 - Pushchairs (5)

2 - Connoisseur (7)

3 - Chemical salt (4)

4 - Route (4)

5 - Compel (5)

6 - Separators (7)

8 - Using (9)

12 - Male person (3)

13 - Representation (3)

14 - Damaged (7)

16 - Changes gradually (7)

18 - Fabric for jeans (5)

21 - Records on tape (5)

22 - Edges (4)

23 - Social insects (4)

Crosswords

Across

1 - Turtle (8)

6 - Pass tongue over (4)

8 - Roman general (6)

9 - Swords (6)

10 - Aeroplane (3)

11 - Shame (4)

12 - Shouted out (6)

13 - Excessively (6)

15 - Stylish (6)

17 - Spurts (6)

20 - Leave (4)

21 - Intelligence (3)

22 - Defence (6)

23 - Yield (6)

24 - Underside (4)

25 - Island S of Australia (8)

Down

2 - Avoidance (7)

3 - Irritable (5)

4 - False testimony (7)

5 - Beastly (5)

6 - Garden flower (7)

7 - Pancake (5)

14 - Uncommon (7)

15 - Boxes (7)

16 - Nerve impulses (7)

18 - Fairy (5)

19 - Dessert (5)

20 - Excess (5)

Crosswords

Across

1 - Straightened (6)

3 - Companionless (6)

7 - Violent upheaval (9)

9 - Dissentious (8)

10 - Small island (4)

12 - Secret agents (5)

13 - Abstraction (5)

17 - Goes (anag) (4)

18 - Move (8)

20 - Skullcaps (9)

21 - Wipeout (6)

22 - Capital of Canada (6)

Down

1 - Elevation (6)

2 - Chemical fertilisers (8)

4 - Chalcedony (4)

5 - Freeholders (6)

6 - Set piece in rugby (5)

7 - Dissonance (9)

8 - Players (9)

11 - Cog; chain wheel (8)

14 - Drinking cup (6)

15 - Happen again (5)

16 - Swiss city (6)

19 - Amphibian (4)

Crosswords

Across

1 - Sour taste (8)
6 - Retail store (4)
8 - Exploited (6)
9 - Expressed (6)
10 - Greek letter (3)
11 - Long (4)
12 - Refill (6)
13 - Epic (6)
15 - Capital of Greece (6)
17 - Brambles (6)
20 - Court enclosure (4)
21 - Smack (3)
22 - Elaborately adorned (6)
23 - Shun (6)
24 - Leg joint (4)
25 - Farm enclosure (8)

Down

2 - Outer ear (7)
3 - Herb (5)
4 - Relating to a disease (7)
5 - Give a solemn oath (5)
6 - Squash (7)
7 - Last Greek letter (5)
14 - Direct or control (7)
15 - Non-professional (7)
16 - ___power;power from uranium (7)
18 - Repeat (5)
19 - Ridge (5)
20 - Decomposition (5)

Crosswords

Across

1 - Decency (7)

4 - Higher (5)

7 - Journal (5)

8 - Operated (7)

9 - Big cat (4)

10 - Surpass (3)

11 - Complain (4)

15 - Soundproofing (9)

17 - Unravel (4)

19 - Hurried (3)

20 - Get better (4)

24 - Fatness (7)

25 - Eg oxygen; nitrogen (5)

26 - Plant fibre (5)

27 - Naturists (7)

Down

1 - Scale representation (5)

2 - Sparkler (7)

3 - Inflammation of an eyelid (4)

4 - State in the W United States (4)

5 - Lively Bohemian dance (5)

6 - Enigmas (7)

8 - Single-humped camel (9)

12 - Negative (3)

13 - Ease into chair (3)

14 - Strident (7)

16 - Oils (7)

18 - Judges (5)

21 - Endures (5)

22 - Clock face (4)

23 - Developed (4)

Crosswords

Across

1 - Slender coiling leaves (8)

6 - Pleasingly pretty (4)

8 - Remunerate (6)

9 - Being inactive (6)

10 - Arab Emirates (abbrev) (3)

11 - Secure cabinet (4)

12 - Of delicate beauty (6)

13 - Top quality (6)

15 - Continent (6)

17 - Horse restraint (6)

20 - Belonging to us (4)

21 - Small truck (3)

22 - Spain and Portugal (6)

23 - Greatest of the Egyptian gods (6)

24 - Abstract Spanish artist (4)

25 - Avoidances (8)

Down

2 - Raise up (7)

3 - Semiconductor (5)

4 - Sudden inclination to act (7)

5 - Travelled on snow runners (5)

6 - Coal miner (7)

7 - Dogma (5)

14 - Experience (7)

15 - Benign tumour (7)

16 - Raw meat (7)

18 - Spiritual leader (5)

19 - Avoid (5)

20 - Small antelope (5)

Crosswords

Across

1 - Liable to change (7)

4 - Conceals (5)

7 - Palpitate (5)

8 - Residence of the Pope (7)

9 - Platform (4)

10 - Deciduous tree (3)

11 - Funeral pile (4)

15 - Those who live for pleasure (9)

17 - One less than ten (4)

19 - Protective cover (3)

20 - Trickery (4)

24 - Isolate (7)

25 - Steering systems (5)

26 - Provide (5)

27 - Changed (7)

Down

1 - Hushed (5)

2 - Sully (7)

3 - Moves up and down (4)

4 - Smacks (4)

5 - Lure (5)

6 - Offenders (7)

8 - Sweetheart (9)

12 - Lyric poem (3)

13 - Tree (3)

14 - Veracity (7)

16 - Long fishing line (7)

18 - Mother-of-pearl (5)

21 - Loosened (5)

22 - Regretted (4)

23 - Close (4)

Crosswords

Across

1 - Boundless (8)

6 - Paper money (4)

8 - Needle (6)

9 - Destroy (6)

10 - Soft-finned fish (3)

11 - Wander (4)

12 - Tracks (6)

13 - Sports equipment (6)

15 - Toffees (6)

17 - Oozes out (6)

20 - Converse (4)

21 - Variety (3)

22 - Innate (6)

23 - Use (6)

24 - Leg joint (4)

25 - Hangs down (8)

Down

2 - Communication system (7)

3 - Religious faith of Muslims (5)

4 - Slips in (7)

5 - Show triumphant joy (5)

6 - Heart-shaped (7)

7 - Decay (5)

14 - Larva of frogs (7)

15 - Finders (7)

16 - Instructed (7)

18 - Colourless inert gas (5)

19 - Nasal passageway (5)

20 - Small woodland (5)

Crosswords

Across

1 - Destitution (6)

4 - Polish composer and pianist (6)

9 - Still image; dramatic scene (7)

10 - Tell (7)

11 - Summons (5)

12 - Abrasive material (5)

14 - Narrow openings (5)

15 - Lower floor of church (5)

17 - Rule (5)

18 - Sour cherry (7)

20 - Self important (7)

21 - Produces (6)

22 - Exploited (6)

Down

1 - Coup (6)

2 - Exalted moral excellence (8)

3 - Smells (5)

5 - Funeral cars (7)

6 - Insect stage (4)

7 - Import (6)

8 - Strict (11)

13 - Ability to produce a desired result (8)

14 - Halted (7)

15 - Conform (6)

16 - Joined together (6)

17 - Vertical part of a step (5)

19 - Commit to memory (4)

Crosswords

1	■	2	■	3	■	■	■	4	■	5	■	6
7						■	8					
	■		■		■	9	■		■		■	
10							■	11				
	■		■		■		■		■		■	
12				■	13					■	■	■
	■		■	14	■		■		■	15	■	16
■	■	■	17					■	18			
19	■	20	■		■		■	21	■		■	
22					■	23						
	■		■		■		■		■		■	
24						■	25					
	■		■		■	■	■		■		■	

Across

7 - Free from danger (6)

8 - Subject to death (6)

10 - Height (7)

11 - Guide (5)

12 - A fitting reward (4)

13 - Duties (5)

17 - Not odds (5)

18 - Ice mass (4)

22 - Conclude (5)

23 - Give authority to (7)

24 - Sled (6)

25 - Communicate (6)

Down

1 - Expect (7)

2 - Trialled or tested (7)

3 - Musical movement (5)

4 - Abandon (7)

5 - Aquatic mammal (5)

6 - Promotional wording (5)

9 - Something left over (9)

14 - Antiquated (7)

15 - Clutching (7)

16 - Walking stick cap (7)

19 - In the middle of (5)

20 - Later (5)

21 - Kingdom in SW Europe (5)

Crosswords

Across

1 - Very hot day (8)

6 - Curse; solemn promise (4)

8 - Shout (6)

9 - Hurls (6)

10 - Annoy (3)

11 - Feathered creature (4)

12 - Not dense (6)

13 - Struck by overwhelming shock (6)

15 - Leaders (6)

17 - Tropical fly (6)

20 - Spoollike toy (4)

21 - Arrest (3)

22 - Abominable (6)

23 - Self-supporting structures (6)

24 - Horse breeding farm (4)

25 - Material used as a colourant (8)

Down

2 - Preparing food (7)

3 - Disturbed (5)

4 - Kidney bean (7)

5 - Dangers (5)

6 - Paper folding (7)

7 - Roman cloaks (5)

14 - Changed (7)

15 - Vegetable (7)

16 - Page in a book (7)

18 - Fire a weapon (5)

19 - Finished (5)

20 - Water vessel (5)

Crosswords

Across

1 - Seizes ownership of (6)

3 - Renovate (6)

7 - Anglers (9)

9 - Worthy of great honour (8)

10 - Snob (4)

12 - Musical study piece (5)

13 - Opinions (5)

17 - Sailing ship (4)

18 - Cut (8)

20 - Represent (9)

21 - Erase (6)

22 - Business organisation (6)

Down

1 - Huggable (6)

2 - Wrongdoings (8)

4 - Trees (4)

5 - Fall (6)

6 - Written passages (5)

7 - Ornamental water jets (9)

8 - Pertaining to a standard (9)

11 - Looking up to (8)

14 - Utterly senseless (6)

15 - Labour organisation (5)

16 - Charles Schulz' beagle (6)

19 - Soot particle (4)

Crosswords

Across

1 - Met (7)

4 - Brass instrument (5)

7 - Metal shaping machine (5)

8 - Orange vegetables (7)

9 - Colour properties (4)

10 - And not (3)

11 - Gemstone (4)

15 - Enticement (9)

17 - Monetary unit of South Africa (4)

19 - Damp (3)

20 - Comply (4)

24 - Child's room (7)

25 - Sweet scented shrub (5)

26 - Prayers (5)

27 - Capital of Indonesia (7)

Down

1 - Grime and dirt (5)

2 - Places of business (7)

3 - Hinge joint (4)

4 - Capital of Switzerland (4)

5 - Assembly (5)

6 - Fifth Greek letter (7)

8 - Eccentric (9)

12 - Increase (3)

13 - Impertinence (slang) (3)

14 - Edible root (7)

16 - Biter (7)

18 - Norwegian (5)

21 - House plant (5)

22 - Limbs (4)

23 - Antiaircraft fire (4)

Crosswords

Across

1 - Tips and instruction (6)

3 - Writings (6)

7 - Heavy Winter garment (9)

9 - Interfered with (8)

10 - Among (4)

12 - Group (5)

13 - Cutlery (5)

17 - One of a matching pair (4)

18 - Agreeable (8)

20 - Death rate (9)

21 - Tension (6)

22 - More gruesome (6)

Down

1 - Allows (6)

2 - Belief (8)

4 - Clog (4)

5 - Criticises (6)

6 - Opposite one of two (5)

7 - Room for indoor sports (9)

8 - Not permanent (9)

11 - Sprinkling with water (8)

14 - Large pebbles (6)

15 - Fastening device (5)

16 - Unconsciousness (6)

19 - Time periods (4)

Crosswords

Across

1 - Short heavy club (8)

6 - Thought (4)

8 - Walk with long steps (6)

9 - Steep-sided valley (6)

10 - Vitality (3)

11 - Sovereign (4)

12 - Vital essence (6)

13 - Drink (6)

15 - Cloth covering arm (6)

17 - Feigns (6)

20 - Flesh of a hog (4)

21 - Sharp implement (3)

22 - Compensate for (6)

23 - Learned person (6)

24 - Fitness centres (4)

25 - Company head (8)

Down

2 - Soft metallic element (7)

3 - Executing (5)

4 - Lift up (7)

5 - Standards (5)

6 - Financial statement (7)

7 - Boredom (5)

14 - Fills with (7)

15 - Type of spy (7)

16 - Fear of heights (7)

18 - Towering (5)

19 - Satisfied (5)

20 - Feeling of fear (5)

Crosswords

1				2		■	3	4				5
	■	■	■		■	6	■		■	■	■	
	■	7								8	■	
	■		■		■		■		■		■	
9								■	10			
	■		■		■		■	11	■		■	
■	12					■	13					■
14	■		■		■	15	■		■		■	16
17				■	18							
	■		■	19	■		■		■		■	
	■	20									■	
	■	■	■		■		■		■	■	■	
21						■	22					

Across

1 - Dispute (6)

3 - Terminated (6)

7 - Square dance (9)

9 - Inflammation of the nose (8)

10 - Gnus (anag) (4)

12 - Russian monarchs (5)

13 - Board game (5)

17 - Agreement (4)

18 - Fail to notice (8)

20 - Suppleness (9)

21 - Deforms (6)

22 - Make beloved (6)

Down

1 - Smells (6)

2 - Glass workers (8)

4 - Rhythmic quality (4)

5 - Injure (6)

6 - Distinguishing characteristic (5)

7 - Comical (9)

8 - Paint coatings (9)

11 - Bakers dozen (8)

14 - Leafy vegetable; grow (6)

15 - Vines (5)

16 - Ice mover (6)

19 - Destroy (4)

Crosswords

1		2		3				4		5		6
7							8					
						9						
10								11				
12					13							
				14						15		16
			17						18			
19		20						21				
22						23						
24							25					

Across

7 - Permed (6)

8 - Tempt (6)

10 - Develop beyond (7)

11 - Baby garment (5)

12 - Device for securing (4)

13 - Office person (5)

17 - Sharpener (5)

18 - Big cat (4)

22 - Moved back and forth (5)

23 - Conceited person (7)

24 - Pertaining to the teeth (6)

25 - Royal chair (6)

Down

1 - Manuscripts (7)

2 - Judges (7)

3 - Mocks (5)

4 - Deceive (7)

5 - Walks awkwardly (5)

6 - Precious stone (5)

9 - Ate (9)

14 - Symbols of disgrace (7)

15 - Chemical element (7)

16 - One more (7)

19 - Apart from (5)

20 - Overcooked (5)

21 - Variety of coffee (5)

Crosswords

Across

1 - Common bird (6)

7 - Volcanic glass (8)

8 - And not (3)

9 - Wrangle (6)

10 - Ark builder (4)

11 - Governed (5)

13 - Informs (7)

15 - Manned (7)

17 - Inquired (5)

21 - White soft mineral (4)

22 - Believer in God (6)

23 - First on list (3)

24 - Summer squash (8)

25 - Debt that remains unpaid (6)

Down

1 - Provide for (6)

2 - Rodent (6)

3 - Sheltered places (5)

4 - Supplanted (7)

5 - Lymph nodes (8)

6 - Misleading fabrication (6)

12 - Brings intended result (8)

14 - Confident (7)

16 - Drinking vessel (6)

18 - Pot (6)

19 - Nappy (6)

20 - Newspapers and TV (5)

Crosswords

Across

1 - Relaxed (7)

4 - Create by hammering (5)

7 - Bird droppings (5)

8 - Unpredictable (7)

9 - Inhabitant of Denmark (4)

10 - Quantity of money (3)

11 - Selfish person (4)

15 - Baton (9)

17 - Particles (4)

19 - Posed (3)

20 - Agitate (4)

24 - Furnish (7)

25 - Bird claw (5)

26 - Tries out (5)

27 - Nasal cavities (7)

Down

1 - Advised (5)

2 - Oddity (7)

3 - On top of (4)

4 - Ire (4)

5 - Religious acts (5)

6 - Extract (7)

8 - Proclaim (9)

12 - Shelter (3)

13 - Born (3)

14 - Fragment (7)

16 - Stinging weeds (7)

18 - On son (anag) (5)

21 - Leases (5)

22 - Drinks (4)

23 - English public school (4)

Crosswords

Across

1 - Substitute kept in reserve (6)

7 - Waver (8)

8 - By way of (3)

9 - Italian sausage (6)

10 - Caresses (4)

11 - Pen-like tools (5)

13 - Adhesive label (7)

15 - Kingdom in N Europe (7)

17 - Aviator (5)

21 - Republic in SW Asia (4)

22 - Groups of animals (6)

23 - Arab Emirates (abbrev) (3)

24 - Runs machinery (8)

25 - Flings (6)

Down

1 - Angled edges (6)

2 - Stylish (6)

3 - Bottle (5)

4 - Aids (7)

5 - Abnormal (8)

6 - Sculpture (6)

12 - Celestial body (8)

14 - Learned (7)

16 - Continent (6)

18 - Topics for debate (6)

19 - Streams (6)

20 - Raise (5)

Crosswords

Across

7 - Grow teeth (6)

8 - Input device (6)

10 - Shut in (7)

11 - Line of work (5)

12 - City in NW France (4)

13 - Kingdom (5)

17 - Misses out (5)

18 - Soft drink (4)

22 - Fabric with parallel ribs (5)

23 - Tensing (anag) (7)

24 - Type of sausage (6)

25 - Tennis player ___ Williams (6)

Down

1 - Expansive movement (7)

2 - Instructor (7)

3 - Fire a weapon (5)

4 - Writing implements (7)

5 - Spiked weapon (5)

6 - Modifies (5)

9 - Fixing (9)

14 - Symbols (7)

15 - Announcements (7)

16 - Public executioner (7)

19 - Hiding place (5)

20 - Daft (5)

21 - Popular R&B performer (5)

Crosswords

Across

1 - Spain and Portugal (6)

4 - Fumed (6)

9 - Warning (7)

10 - Specialist traders (7)

11 - Dust particles (5)

12 - Advised (5)

14 - Live by (5)

15 - Passenger ship (5)

17 - One over par (golf) (5)

18 - Agitate (7)

20 - Person who keeps watch (7)

21 - Sewing instrument (6)

22 - Soft mineral: plaster of Paris (6)

Down

1 - Financial gain (6)

2 - Violent discharge (8)

3 - Vines (5)

5 - Short-tailed monkey (7)

6 - Bird of prey (4)

7 - Extinguished (6)

8 - Objectionable (11)

13 - Beautiful (8)

14 - State of readiness (7)

15 - Subatomic particle (6)

16 - Method (6)

17 - Ungainly sea bird (5)

19 - Flower (4)

Crosswords

Across

1 - Alter (7)

4 - Chocolate powder (5)

7 - Volume measure (5)

8 - Causes (7)

9 - Deserve (4)

10 - Entirely (3)

11 - Nervy (4)

15 - Wriggly (9)

17 - Written communication (4)

19 - Fool (3)

20 - Understand (4)

24 - Large spotted cat (7)

25 - Loathe (5)

26 - Fish dish (5)

27 - Break into pieces (7)

Down

1 - Edible lentil (5)

2 - Comes back (7)

3 - Sued (anag) (4)

4 - Thick lump of blood (4)

5 - Cloaked (5)

6 - Analyst (7)

8 - Divided (9)

12 - Effigy (3)

13 - Appropriate (3)

14 - Skin eruptions (7)

16 - Shooting noise (7)

18 - Stars (5)

21 - Electrician (5)

22 - Hired form of transport (4)

23 - Celebration (4)

Crosswords

Across

7 - Republic in SW Asia (6)

8 - Legendary king of Britain (6)

10 - Avoidance (7)

11 - Diversion (5)

12 - Wild mountain goat (4)

13 - Darken (5)

17 - Glosses over (5)

18 - Vend (4)

22 - Disgust (5)

23 - Stormy (7)

24 - Winter sport (6)

25 - Earn; store grain (6)

Down

1 - Republic in W Africa (7)

2 - Visionary (7)

3 - Winding shape (5)

4 - Unpredictable (7)

5 - Waterslide (5)

6 - Armistice (5)

9 - Closest to the centre (9)

14 - Horizon (7)

15 - Effective (7)

16 - Killers (7)

19 - Cease (5)

20 - Ruin (5)

21 - One of the United Arab Emirates (5)

Crosswords

1 2 3 4 5 6 7 8 9 10 11 12 13 14 15 16 17 18 19 20 21 22

Across

1 - Facial gestures (6)

3 - Assessments (6)

7 - Difficulties (9)

9 - Complains (8)

10 - Proper (4)

12 - Common tree (5)

13 - Ancient (5)

17 - Exchange (4)

18 - Curling hair (8)

20 - Strongly disapproving of (9)

21 - Repeat from memory (6)

22 - True statement (6)

Down

1 - Living room (6)

2 - Type of book cover (8)

4 - Rotary motion (4)

5 - Herb with oil rich seeds (6)

6 - Inquired (5)

7 - Female servant (9)

8 - Measuring (9)

11 - More awkward (8)

14 - Line of pressure (6)

15 - The Hunter (5)

16 - Self interest (6)

19 - Mark or blemish (4)

Crosswords

1	■	2	■	3	■	■	■	4	■	5	■	6
7						■	8					
	■		■		■	9	■		■		■	
10							■	11				
	■		■		■		■		■		■	
12				■	13					■	■	■
	■		■	14	■		■		■	15	■	16
■	■	■	17					■	18			
19	■	20	■		■		■	21	■		■	
22					■	23						
	■		■		■		■		■		■	
24						■	25					
	■		■		■	■	■		■		■	

Across

7 - Whole (6)

8 - Imposter (6)

10 - Schedule of activities (7)

11 - Waste meat (5)

12 - Having pains (4)

13 - Instruct (5)

17 - Attendant upon God (5)

18 - Pose (anag) (4)

22 - Queen's favourite dog (5)

23 - Donations to those in need (7)

24 - Steering mechanism (6)

25 - Edge (6)

Down

1 - Demonstration (7)

2 - Waste away (7)

3 - Earth colour (5)

4 - Diffusion of fluids (7)

5 - Polishes (5)

6 - Absurdity (5)

9 - Coming out (9)

14 - Provoked (7)

15 - Attack (7)

16 - Imitative (7)

19 - Written form of music (5)

20 - Philosophical system (5)

21 - Polite address for a woman (5)

Crosswords

1		2			3	■	4	■	5	■	6	■
	■		■	■	7							
8			■	■		■		■		■		■
	■	9						■	10			
	■		■	■		■		■		■		■
11			12		■	13						
■	■	■		■	14	■		■		■	■	■
15	16						■	17		18		19
■		■		■		■	20	■	■		■	
21				■	22						■	
■		■		■		■		■	■	23		
24								■	■		■	
■		■		■		■	25					

Across

1 - Globule of air (6)

7 - Sales (8)

8 - Boy (3)

9 - Be contingent upon (6)

10 - Fencing sword (4)

11 - Finely cut straw (5)

13 - General pardon (7)

15 - Kingdom in W Europe (7)

17 - Religious writing (5)

21 - Hire (4)

22 - Instrumental piece (6)

23 - 19th Greek letter (3)

24 - Food portions (8)

25 - Composer (6)

Down

1 - European sea (6)

2 - Indian religious leader (6)

3 - Long ___ owl (5)

4 - Learning institution (7)

5 - Inanimate (8)

6 - Meaning (6)

12 - Runaway (8)

14 - Style of cooking (7)

16 - Small hole (6)

18 - Diminished (6)

19 - Reciprocal (6)

20 - Grind together (5)

Crosswords

Across

1 - Beauty treatment (6)

4 - Sudden flash; stripe (6)

9 - Back pain (7)

10 - Curved upward (7)

11 - Decay (5)

12 - Wept (5)

14 - Cause (5)

15 - Worn-out (5)

17 - Relative magnitude (5)

18 - Ball shaped objects (7)

20 - Noisiest (7)

21 - Personify (6)

22 - Complied (6)

Down

1 - Lumberjack (6)

2 - Serene (8)

3 - With speed (5)

5 - Divide into three parts (7)

6 - Relaxation (4)

7 - Pleated (6)

8 - Politely (11)

13 - Madly (8)

14 - Beautified (7)

15 - Bump against (6)

16 - Fixed and absolute (6)

17 - Small explosive device (5)

19 - Plant with flavour (4)

Crosswords

Across

1 - Two channel audio (6)

7 - Pertaining to the chest (8)

8 - Foot extremity (3)

9 - Smallest quantities (6)

10 - Deceptive manoeuvre (4)

11 - Writes down (5)

13 - Attendant (7)

15 - Imperfections (7)

17 - Strips of land (5)

21 - Clustering (4)

22 - Novice (6)

23 - Part of mouth (3)

24 - Once every year (8)

25 - Fish eating hawk (6)

Down

1 - Sixth planet (6)

2 - Absolve (6)

3 - Nerve in the eye (5)

4 - Rubbed (7)

5 - Capital of Liberia (8)

6 - Dried grape (6)

12 - Momentous (8)

14 - Surprise (7)

16 - Resembling a horse (6)

18 - Removes outer skin (6)

19 - Slushy (6)

20 - Capital of Japan (5)

Crosswords

Across

1 - Fish or meat dishes (8)

6 - Half burnt coal (4)

8 - Plan of action (6)

9 - Free of an obstruction (6)

10 - Large unit (3)

11 - Conscription (4)

12 - Waterproof overshoe (6)

13 - Loan shark (6)

15 - Makes financial guarantee (6)

17 - Soak up (6)

20 - Young deer (4)

21 - Exclamation of surprise (3)

22 - Rags (6)

23 - Eskimo buildings (6)

24 - Hind part (4)

25 - Maker of machinery (8)

Down

2 - Access (7)

3 - As on the beach (5)

4 - Skin of animal (7)

5 - Smarted (5)

6 - Laughs unpleasantly (7)

7 - Round handles (5)

14 - Male chicken (7)

15 - Irritating (7)

16 - Amended (7)

18 - Attractive young lady (5)

19 - Moisten meat (5)

20 - Criminal (5)

Crosswords

Across

1 - Small portion or share (6)

4 - Respiratory illness (6)

9 - Written record (7)

10 - Eight sided polygon (7)

11 - Strength (5)

12 - Way in (5)

14 - Colour of grass (5)

15 - Sea bird deposit (5)

17 - Inactive (5)

18 - Round of applause (7)

20 - Vary speaking pitch (7)

21 - Oppose (6)

22 - Exploited (6)

Down

1 - Title for a woman (6)

2 - Badge (8)

3 - Make impure (5)

5 - Score less four (7)

6 - Fastened; suspended (4)

7 - Business organisation (6)

8 - Doubtful (11)

13 - Felony (8)

14 - Female deity (7)

15 - Ground squirrel (6)

16 - Proposed (6)

17 - Conclude (5)

19 - Top serves (4)

Crosswords

Across

7 - Stopped (6)

8 - Vestiges (6)

10 - Communicators (7)

11 - Children (5)

12 - Stitches (4)

13 - Facial hair (5)

17 - Inhabitants of Ireland (5)

18 - Blessing (4)

22 - Mistaken (5)

23 - Heroic poem (7)

24 - Slacken (6)

25 - Selected (6)

Down

1 - Crisp (7)

2 - Indian tents (7)

3 - Smiles radiantly (5)

4 - Petitions to God (7)

5 - Cleanse (5)

6 - Custom (5)

9 - Type of waterwheel (9)

14 - Starts (7)

15 - Be made of (7)

16 - Desiring (7)

19 - Alert (5)

20 - Happy; jovial (5)

21 - Legends (5)

Popular Pastimes

R	D	O	B	A	Q	U	T	U	I	F	U	L	R	T
G	H	C	G	R	M	H	B	D	E	F	X	K	O	F
S	U	R	N	G	E	E	A	S	T	W	M	A	O	P
D	I	K	I	P	P	W	N	C	R	G	O	A	G	R
O	K	Y	K	H	U	G	I	I	U	N	V	S	I	A
I	U	B	O	O	M	N	T	N	C	I	I	F	R	R
T	W	O	O	T	O	I	Z	O	G	C	E	T	W	E
Y	E	A	C	O	N	T	N	R	E	A	S	N	A	A
O	B	R	C	G	T	U	X	T	E	R	P	N	L	D
U	S	D	D	R	O	P	O	C	J	R	O	R	K	I
R	I	G	I	A	M	M	S	E	Y	A	R	A	I	N
S	T	A	M	P	C	O	L	L	E	C	T	I	N	G
E	E	M	U	H	R	C	J	E	S	N	S	R	G	L
L	S	E	W	Y	R	T	S	I	M	E	H	C	V	R
F	I	S	T	F	A	R	C	I	S	U	M	R	L	U

Arts
Board Games
Brewing
Car Racing
Chemistry
Cinema
Computing
Cooking
Crafts
Do It Yourself
Electronics
Movies
Music
Photography
Reading
Sports
Stamp Collecting
Walking
Websites
Writing

At the Inn

T	Y	S	S	T	H	E	C	R	O	S	S	A	Q	R
S	R	A	B	T	H	E	R	A	I	L	W	A	Y	O
R	S	D	N	U	O	H	D	N	A	X	O	F	O	Y
A	S	A	A	T	P	U	N	I	C	O	R	N	U	A
G	A	E	P	E	T	H	E	C	H	U	R	C	H	L
L	P	H	V	W	H	I	T	E	B	E	A	R	E	S
A	M	S	R	E	T	S	E	R	O	F	E	H	T	T
F	O	G	A	Y	E	T	G	N	T	Y	E	S	T	A
A	C	A	R	O	S	E	A	N	D	C	R	O	W	N
R	E	N	B	S	P	M	R	S	I	L	H	P	Z	D
T	H	E	R	O	Y	A	L	O	A	K	T	G	K	A
E	T	H	E	C	R	I	C	K	E	T	E	R	S	R
H	D	T	H	E	S	Q	U	A	R	E	S	H	D	D
T	C	V	G	C	R	O	W	A	N	D	G	A	T	E
Q	G	S	A	O	R	P	J	S	T	A	A	N	W	O

Bars
Crow And Gate
Fox And Hounds
Pubs
Rose And Crown
Royal Standard
The Church
The Compass
The Cricketers
The Cross
The Foresters
The King's Head
The Nag's Head
The Railway
The Royal Oak
The Square
The Trafalgar
Three Arrows
Unicorn
White Bear

World A-M

I O A N S G S U R N P O R O Y
M H N O C I X E M A L T A A R
A Q A U C K H A S Y U A A X R
V I P I L R L M O N A C O J A
R R A S B A E A F E G I D N B
K A J B Y M B J I K C R V A B
H C R S R N A O N E O F U L X
O S I J O E N G L D I A N G J
B A B I C D O A A I E Z E B T
U G E O C T N U N F V I E E R
K A I D O D C L D P V I H Q S
A D S R R E V S R L Q D A H C
I A I L O G N O M A D R I D R
B M V A M V B M N P I B T A S
L Z Y T E J B T Z O H A I E O

Africa
Bolivia
Chad
Denmark
Ecuador
Finland
Gambia
Haiti
Iceland
Japan
Kenya
Lebanon
Madagascar
Madrid
Malaysia
Malta
Mexico
Monaco
Mongolia
Morocco

In the Kitchen

O	X	Q	S	Q	E	S	L	Z	S	S	W	R	T	R
G	O	I	O	N	M	A	T	C	H	T	F	Q	F	S
O	I	N	E	V	O	P	O	E	S	S	B	W	R	R
U	E	I	E	J	W	O	L	G	U	L	T	I	W	S
I	A	O	C	E	P	F	P	H	S	U	F	A	S	E
B	U	T	T	E	R	D	I	S	H	X	U	A	R	V
W	Q	X	O	V	B	U	U	I	S	T	A	K	D	T
B	A	R	P	A	R	O	T	D	O	O	R	R	D	R
N	P	V	W	W	E	E	X	G	T	C	E	L	C	S
E	Y	P	E	O	C	L	N	N	H	P	T	W	Q	R
M	J	H	T	R	I	D	E	I	U	N	S	O	D	L
Q	G	P	S	C	L	N	N	V	A	L	A	F	O	V
I	F	K	N	I	S	A	T	R	E	R	O	A	U	Q
M	E	R	E	M	A	C	R	E	M	I	T	G	G	E
K	Z	I	L	U	Q	L	A	S	O	T	S	S	H	O

Butter Dish
Candle
China
Dough
Egg Timer
Ice-box
Match
Microwave
Oven
Scoop
Serving Dish
Shelf
Sieve
Sink
Slicer
Spoon
Stewpot
Strainer
Toaster
Tureen

Feeling Parky

Y	G	T	W	S	J	S	T	N	J	A	T	A	R	Z
P	B	T	E	A	S	P	Z	U	S	A	L	O	Y	R
S	U	R	L	M	L	A	J	K	W	I	H	V	S	S
R	T	E	O	P	O	K	R	I	I	S	T	A	W	S
R	T	E	Z	O	J	Z	E	G	N	E	A	O	K	A
B	E	S	D	U	K	W	C	R	G	E	P	O	T	Z
Q	R	I	A	H	S	E	R	F	S	S	T	O	D	F
L	C	E	R	U	T	N	E	V	D	A	O	A	V	L
E	U	A	E	R	A	Y	A	L	P	W	O	A	A	O
U	P	S	T	T	B	U	T	T	E	R	F	L	Y	W
Q	Z	H	A	U	E	P	I	G	E	O	N	S	P	E
R	N	R	W	R	N	D	O	G	W	A	L	K	E	R
K	T	U	O	B	A	D	N	U	O	R	U	A	O	S
P	A	B	T	A	O	J	R	L	E	P	O	F	Z	L
P	E	S	T	A	T	E	A	B	I	B	U	G	Y	U

Adventure
Brook
Buttercup
Butterfly
Dog Walker
Estate
Flowers
Footpath
Fresh Air
Grass
Pigeons
Play Area
Recreation
Roundabout
See Saw
Shrubs
Swings
Trees
Walkers
Water

Religion

T	D	I	T	M	D	J	B	E	R	U	H	V	O	A
Y	S	N	L	A	J	O	N	A	H	K	Z	E	W	T
F	A	I	O	L	A	P	O	C	S	I	P	E	S	G
C	B	D	D	M	T	S	I	N	I	V	L	A	C	R
U	M	N	S	O	R	W	T	R	E	H	S	O	K	E
R	B	R	O	M	H	O	P	N	H	T	A	B	C	E
D	O	V	U	I	O	T	M	S	Q	R	L	A	H	K
P	C	U	D	F	T	O	E	K	S	H	V	R	R	O
M	A	N	N	A	R	A	D	M	E	V	A	M	I	R
Q	J	O	H	N	T	H	E	B	A	P	T	I	S	T
H	O	L	Y	Y	E	A	R	R	P	A	I	T	T	H
P	A	R	A	B	L	E	Y	R	C	Y	O	Z	I	O
U	E	B	M	E	W	S	L	Y	T	U	N	V	A	D
S	T	V	W	S	F	A	L	L	O	F	M	A	N	O
J	Z	O	R	E	O	W	Z	A	R	S	M	H	H	X

Bar Mitzvah
Calvinist
Christian
Creation
Doomsday
Episcopal
Fall Of Man
Greek Orthodox
Hebrews
Holy Year
Jacob
John The Baptist
Jonah
Kosher
Manna
Methodist
Mormon
Parable
Redemption
Salvation

Smoke and Fire

S	I	E	A	N	C	S	M	O	K	E	F	S	U	S
R	S	L	U	E	J	O	P	E	T	P	Y	A	F	R
L	R	B	P	E	X	T	U	R	A	J	R	O	I	I
L	J	B	S	N	O	F	R	G	E	C	A	T	R	R
A	F	U	G	I	M	I	E	S	H	A	I	T	E	A
I	X	R	D	G	U	W	H	G	M	I	D	V	M	J
A	O	N	O	N	W	A	S	M	R	W	N	I	A	I
Z	F	I	R	E	B	R	I	G	A	D	E	G	N	T
E	P	N	H	E	A	M	U	M	L	A	C	E	A	G
S	G	G	R	R	T	T	G	B	A	P	N	T	O	T
T	J	R	S	I	A	H	N	O	I	T	I	N	G	I
A	L	O	R	F	D	R	I	R	E	N	C	Z	A	Q
S	N	P	E	E	U	T	T	Y	G	A	S	H	E	S
P	K	L	V	S	J	I	X	W	D	A	N	G	E	R
T	S	T	E	W	A	T	E	R	I	F	N	O	B	S

Alarm
Arson
Ashes
Bonfire
Burning
Coughing
Danger
Extinguisher
Fire Brigade
Fire Engine
Fireman
Heat
Ignition
Incendiary
Matches
Rubble
Smoke
Spreading
Warmth
Water

Vegetable Feast

W	R	R	S	T	U	O	R	P	S	Q	R	A	L	I
D	C	T	C	O	U	R	G	E	T	T	E	X	Y	T
I	R	D	A	N	D	E	L	I	O	N	I	O	N	N
J	E	A	F	C	P	A	I	L	O	C	C	O	R	B
R	S	X	H	U	C	R	J	C	H	I	C	O	R	Y
A	S	E	C	C	E	T	G	E	S	R	L	B	R	C
T	S	C	A	U	L	I	F	L	O	W	E	R	G	O
H	J	U	B	M	E	C	Q	E	O	M	N	O	R	C
E	O	T	B	B	R	H	T	R	B	A	N	A	U	P
N	D	T	A	E	Y	O	C	I	M	N	E	D	L	R
X	D	E	G	R	V	K	E	A	A	U	F	B	S	S
S	O	L	E	Y	I	E	V	C	B	G	R	E	T	O
E	A	D	A	H	V	I	I	S	A	U	C	A	S	U
R	F	D	J	Y	V	G	H	E	R	K	I	N	L	L
F	T	S	R	Q	T	C	C	S	X	Q	A	P	L	K

Artichoke
Bamboo Shoots
Broad Bean
Broccoli
Cabbage
Cauliflower
Celeriac
Celery
Chard
Chicory

Chive
Courgette
Cress
Cucumber
Dandelion
Fennel
Gherkin
Lettuce
Onion
Sprouts

Computer Terminology

W	K	L	C	A	C	H	E	S	A	B	A	T	A	D
W	C	C	O	N	T	R	O	L	K	E	Y	R	O	C
L	D	Y	M	F	U	R	Y	R	G	U	H	M	H	L
W	P	E	M	I	T	S	S	E	C	C	A	A	E	O
J	D	N	A	B	D	A	O	R	B	I	R	S	U	C
W	Y	C	N	E	T	A	L	U	N	A	D	D	R	O
B	A	U	D	R	A	T	E	N	C	P	D	L	I	T
U	Q	X	P	M	A	E	A	T	T	O	R	Y	S	O
L	U	X	R	O	I	M	E	X	R	T	I	H	T	R
G	H	P	O	U	E	R	P	A	C	K	V	C	I	P
S	B	W	M	S	S	A	R	M	W	S	E	T	C	F
I	H	Y	P	E	R	T	E	X	T	E	A	N	T	L
M	U	L	T	I	T	H	R	E	A	D	I	N	G	T
H	E	T	T	E	L	E	L	L	A	R	A	P	U	A
I	T	Y	U	I	O	L	T	E	A	T	I	S	P	Q

Access Time
Baud Rate
Broadband
Byte
Cache
Character Set
Command Prompt
Control Key
Database
Desktop
Domain Name
Hard Drive
Heuristic
Hypertext
Latency
Mouse
Multi-threading
Parallel
Parity
Protocol

Visit to the Circus

T	S	I	T	R	A	S	R	P	W	R	S	V	D	P
A	N	I	M	A	L	S	L	L	L	C	L	U	N	M
C	K	E	M	I	M	O	T	N	A	P	E	A	U	J
F	I	L	M	Q	O	U	U	I	S	E	M	S	U	O
L	C	A	N	N	O	N	R	M	E	Z	A	G	D	S
M	T	E	C	H	I	L	D	R	E	N	G	B	R	Y
S	R	L	C	A	Y	A	E	L	J	L	I	I	M	R
C	A	C	U	R	O	D	T	E	E	Z	C	G	A	A
L	P	Y	S	A	X	W	A	R	H	U	I	D	P	S
P	E	C	T	Z	S	O	S	U	E	W	A	I	N	T
T	Z	I	A	A	C	R	O	B	A	T	N	P	B	W
A	E	N	R	O	S	C	E	J	W	A	N	P	M	O
R	E	U	D	R	I	N	G	M	A	S	T	E	R	H
T	E	K	C	U	B	I	G	T	O	P	L	R	L	P
P	L	T	U	T	C	L	O	W	N	S	A	U	Y	F

Acrobat
Animals
Artist
Big Dipper
Big Top
Bucket
Cannon
Children
Clowns
Crowd
Custard
Entertainment
Jugglers
Magician
Pantomime
Ringmaster
Somersault
Trapeze
Unicycle
Wheel

At the Seaside

W	L	R	I	T	L	U	E	V	B	W	K	A	W	V
A	L	W	D	N	A	S	Z	B	R	P	V	K	L	I
V	D	I	J	S	R	O	I	A	Q	W	T	E	O	E
E	A	P	M	A	O	S	C	R	D	D	M	Y	R	U
S	G	S	O	P	C	K	E	N	T	P	U	U	A	M
E	A	R	H	L	E	Q	C	A	I	O	X	N	K	L
A	A	Y	L	E	Y	T	R	C	W	F	S	D	A	M
N	T	C	O	K	M	P	E	L	F	E	F	V	K	P
E	N	O	M	E	N	A	A	E	S	K	E	U	K	I
T	F	T	P	Y	G	O	M	R	Y	R	R	D	P	Y
T	R	E	W	W	C	N	S	H	Y	I	T	I	S	I
L	L	U	G	A	E	S	O	T	P	L	X	U	H	K
E	T	I	G	N	U	F	H	P	Z	L	T	B	M	L
E	G	T	V	X	R	L	E	S	S	U	M	N	W	I
M	M	T	X	W	S	L	Q	L	S	Q	K	R	A	A

Barnacle
Coral
Fungite
Ice cream
Kelp
Krill
Laver
Limpet
Mussel
Polypary
Puffin
Sand
Sea Anemone
Sea Nettle
Seagull
Seaweed
Sponge
Waves
Wrack
Zoophyte

Behind the Camera

Y	S	B	S	O	G	R	U	Y	T	S	V	T	C	J
G	N	I	T	E	K	C	A	R	B	U	L	B	P	X
D	O	C	A	B	L	E	R	E	L	E	A	S	E	P
U	I	W	C	C	A	M	E	R	A	F	S	G	T	V
F	S	F	L	I	O	L	C	R	C	A	G	R	R	G
G	L	S	F	N	O	O	T	E	K	S	N	U	D	T
G	U	B	O	U	N	O	I	T	A	T	I	G	A	C
A	M	I	P	T	S	N	A	L	N	F	S	I	Y	A
P	E	S	R	R	H	E	L	I	D	I	O	E	L	P
E	R	A	S	P	K	P	R	F	W	L	P	U	I	M
R	S	W	O	L	L	E	B	I	H	M	X	L	G	O
T	U	C	E	L	L	U	L	O	I	D	E	O	H	C
U	D	L	E	I	F	F	O	H	T	P	E	D	T	A
R	K	S	Y	G	C	L	O	S	E	U	P	U	Z	D
E	P	W	D	E	V	E	L	O	P	R	I	E	B	T

Agitation
Aperture
Bellows
Black And White
Bracketing
Bulb
Cable Release
Camera
Celluloid
Close Up
Compact
Contrast
Daylight
Depth Of Field
Develop
Diffuser
Emulsion
Exposing
Fast Film
Filter

Making Music

I	H	R	S	V	M	O	T	Q	U	E	X	C	W	N
O	J	N	A	B	Y	K	P	X	C	R	O	I	D	T
P	L	G	J	N	A	I	A	Q	P	P	E	H	K	I
L	D	L	S	H	Q	C	T	P	K	Q	O	S	H	R
T	R	T	E	N	A	T	S	A	C	P	P	S	A	S
M	U	B	P	C	F	R	E	N	C	H	H	O	R	N
E	M	U	I	N	O	H	P	U	E	A	A	N	M	R
M	S	G	P	O	L	Y	I	S	E	O	B	O	O	E
I	P	L	N	O	O	R	P	A	I	T	I	I	N	M
R	E	E	A	S	C	R	G	M	S	C	L	D	I	I
D	H	N	P	S	C	N	A	G	R	O	H	R	U	C
A	S	O	J	A	I	N	B	I	O	A	V	O	M	L
T	Z	F	O	B	P	A	T	S	E	L	E	C	R	U
G	I	F	P	F	A	S	L	A	B	M	Y	C	A	D
C	V	Q	W	Z	P	E	K	E	Y	B	O	A	R	D

Accordion
Bagpipes
Banjo
Bassoon
Bugle
Castanet
Celesta
Cello
Cymbals
Drums
Dulcimer
Euphonium
French Horn
Harmonium
Harpsichord
Keyboard
Oboe
Organ
Panpipes
Piccolo

Names Beginning with 'B'

S	R	Y	T	M	B	E	T	H	A	T	X	I	I	V
B	A	Y	F	J	B	C	X	J	B	A	S	M	T	V
A	B	R	O	Q	H	O	I	A	S	G	M	D	U	S
B	A	R	A	C	K	J	R	E	S	A	C	U	C	X
E	N	A	A	B	N	R	T	I	G	I	E	P	I	H
S	R	B	T	D	R	S	A	S	S	X	Y	P	E	C
E	B	R	B	I	L	A	E	S	P	A	C	L	S	O
F	E	C	N	O	Y	E	B	Q	T	Q	A	I	T	B
R	N	A	I	A	O	T	Y	C	U	O	Y	P	Q	T
W	I	D	M	R	P	T	I	P	R	S	R	R	B	J
I	T	N	A	T	O	D	H	B	L	I	S	A	B	F
P	O	I	J	B	E	R	T	I	E	K	I	E	A	E
H	I	L	N	N	O	E	V	S	H	C	L	D	G	S
I	X	E	E	S	E	T	E	Z	O	L	K	A	X	A
V	S	B	B	A	L	T	A	S	A	R	W	Y	Y	Z

Babe
Baltasar
Barack
Barbara
Barry
Basil
Beatrix
Becky
Belinda
Bella
Benedict
Benito
Benjamin
Bertie
Beth
Beyonce
Bjorn
Booth
Boris
Bradley

At the Movies

D	T	R	Y	A	W	M	D	Y	S	A	T	N	A	F
H	R	O	A	L	D	E	F	R	I	E	N	D	S	E
Q	E	E	C	K	T	R	S	A	A	P	G	P	I	R
T	N	A	T	M	P	Y	E	T	E	M	F	O	S	R
J	O	E	R	S	X	T	D	N	E	S	A	P	Q	O
U	I	E	E	T	U	P	W	E	A	R	U	C	S	S
E	T	I	S	R	T	B	T	M	M	L	N	O	E	S
O	C	R	S	A	C	H	K	U	K	O	I	R	Z	L
M	I	E	E	I	M	S	R	C	A	E	C	N	J	X
T	F	H	S	L	Z	N	E	O	O	W	Q	N	E	S
R	D	S	R	E	L	O	K	D	B	L	O	S	R	R
Y	U	U	O	R	L	I	N	E	I	P	B	M	E	W
M	G	Q	T	S	P	T	R	I	T	W	R	E	L	I
Z	U	R	C	A	S	C	I	H	O	R	R	O	R	U
B	F	K	A	S	T	A	E	S	T	Q	L	H	A	Z

Action
Actors
Actresses
Adrenaline
Blockbuster
Comedy
Documentary
Drama
Fantasy
Fiction
Friends
Heart Throb
Horror
Popcorn
Seats
Thriller
Trailers
Usher
Western
Wide Screen

Countries of Scotland

D	U	N	B	A	R	T	O	N	S	H	I	R	E	W
O	V	D	U	M	F	R	I	E	S	S	H	I	R	E
A	Z	C	J	U	L	X	R	R	S	B	P	Z	I	R
S	I	I	K	T	P	Z	J	Y	E	W	R	L	H	I
M	O	R	A	Y	S	H	I	R	E	I	O	D	S	H
I	I	N	V	E	R	N	E	S	S	E	S	N	N	S
D	I	V	N	A	I	H	T	O	L	T	S	A	E	N
L	S	S	T	I	R	L	I	N	G	I	S	L	E	R
O	P	I	X	J	O	R	K	N	E	Y	H	T	D	I
T	P	E	R	T	H	S	H	I	R	E	I	E	R	A
H	E	F	H	S	W	W	U	Q	M	S	R	H	E	N
I	P	I	B	U	T	E	S	H	I	R	E	S	B	G
A	A	F	P	E	R	I	H	S	K	R	A	N	A	L
N	T	C	A	I	T	H	N	E	S	S	U	G	N	A
K	T	V	I	I	B	E	R	W	I	C	K	N	V	S

Aberdeenshire
Angus
Berwick
Buteshire
Caithness
Dumfriesshire
Dunbartonshire
East Lothian
Fife
Inverness
Lanarkshire
Midlothian
Morayshire
Nairnshire
Orkney
Perthshire
Ross-shire
Shetland
Stirling
West Lothian

Shades and Hues

S Q A E N W T T F U S N P S R
A E Z R S Q A R T D O I I P O
U S H A L I X T Z R E V L I S
T N I T A R R N F A T I S N Q
F K M L S C H E S T N U T K C
R W F A T B M C C S A I P O I
T A E B L E A S Y U D V P S R
T K L O U R R E A M R P U G F
U U N C M R M R N E E P U C R
W D B I V E G O A R V V E R Q
M X N G R R R U G C L D U E N
I E N A V Y B L N R O K U A X
D W L V F W S F U D E T Y M M
A D R P T G A T I C Y E T R D
M H O B X O H G S I E N N A U

Blond
Burgundy
Carmine
Cerise
Chestnut
Cobalt
Copper
Cream
Cyan
Emerald
Fluorescent
Green
Mauve
Mustard
Navy
Pink
Sienna
Silver
Terracotta
Verdant

Drinks

I	I	Q	M	P	K	O	S	R	E	T	S	I	N	A
P	H	S	N	J	Z	L	J	S	A	Z	F	Y	L	L
I	A	F	I	R	Q	B	S	O	A	C	A	R	U	C
Y	P	U	H	K	I	R	S	C	H	E	T	R	S	O
V	A	U	L	G	R	E	N	A	D	I	N	E	C	H
P	K	C	N	M	E	T	A	L	O	C	O	H	C	O
X	O	X	H	C	H	A	R	T	R	E	U	S	E	L
C	I	D	E	R	H	W	I	O	Y	L	R	F	H	I
G	W	Y	R	A	M	Y	D	O	O	L	B	M	L	A
S	G	O	B	E	N	E	D	I	C	T	I	N	E	T
W	O	O	A	P	P	L	E	J	A	C	K	T	C	K
B	U	L	L	B	W	R	M	L	N	U	S	R	C	C
M	D	O	T	S	C	A	P	P	U	C	C	I	N	O
K	N	N	E	T	A	B	S	I	N	T	H	E	Q	C
E	N	G	A	P	M	A	H	C	S	V	J	Y	D	A

Absinthe
Alcohol
Applejack
Barley Water
Benedictine
Bloody Mary
Cappuccino
Champagne
Chartreuse
Chocolate
Cider
Cocktail
Curacao
Grenadine
Herbal Tea
Kirsch
Oolong
Punch
Retsina
Sherry

Types of Tree

U	I	O	U	U	A	W	E	D	V	U	C	C	U	A
A	F	N	R	O	H	T	K	C	U	B	M	U	N	U
I	O	O	B	M	A	B	D	I	L	L	A	I	R	A
T	N	A	E	L	K	W	O	O	D	U	S	Y	U	F
Z	S	U	R	A	T	L	O	H	Q	E	L	S	O	I
V	F	U	O	P	U	S	W	H	E	S	A	L	B	R
E	E	V	H	Y	T	S	N	D	S	P	B	W	M	T
B	P	C	P	R	U	E	E	T	P	R	R	A	A	R
S	I	Q	M	O	N	K	E	Y	P	U	Z	Z	L	E
U	Y	R	A	V	T	F	R	R	Q	C	U	A	A	E
X	H	L	C	I	S	T	G	M	T	E	P	I	C	J
J	J	X	R	H	E	L	C	A	P	M	A	H	C	N
R	E	B	M	A	H	O	G	A	N	Y	L	F	U	L
Y	R	R	E	H	C	R	E	D	C	E	D	A	R	S
S	S	J	S	A	A	H	R	K	W	T	A	K	P	Q

Amber
Aniseed
Balsam
Bamboo
Birch
Blue spruce
Buckthorn
Calambour
Camphor
Champac
Cherry
Chestnut
Elk-wood
Fir Tree
Greenwood
Ivory Palm
Mahogany
Monkey-puzzle
Palm Tree
Red Cedar

A Relaxing Bath

U	T	U	S	U	R	T	U	K	F	T	L	N	P	D
B	U	G	S	L	O	O	P	M	A	H	S	R	U	L
K	S	T	N	E	C	S	L	A	B	R	E	H	I	K
X	L	O	T	I	O	N	T	Y	M	H	I	L	T	S
C	I	T	S	A	S	T	C	S	C	T	R	O	B	M
A	O	A	S	L	E	W	O	T	T	A	T	S	W	H
N	R	N	T	S	S	A	A	P	U	B	E	T	M	O
D	E	U	D	H	K	R	A	W	B	E	L	L	G	E
L	D	A	O	I	C	R	E	A	M	L	I	P	S	X
E	N	W	V	S	T	O	S	S	E	B	O	O	A	Y
S	E	Y	K	D	R	I	Z	H	X	B	T	V	S	R
R	V	C	A	N	N	O	O	I	S	U	I	T	R	Y
H	A	I	R	C	A	R	E	N	I	B	E	T	L	R
B	L	A	Q	S	P	O	N	G	E	A	C	S	P	Q
Q	Q	L	P	R	E	T	A	W	M	R	A	W	K	M

Back Scratcher
Basin
Bubble Bath
Candles
Conditioner
Cream
Hair Care
Herbal Scents
Lavender Oil
Lotion
Shampoo
Shower
Sing
Soak
Sponge
Steam
Toiletries
Towels
Warm Water
Washing

Feeling Fruity

T	P	A	Y	I	A	G	U	E	J	N	N	P	G	H
R	I	Y	R	R	E	B	N	A	R	C	L	T	Z	C
E	N	I	R	A	T	C	E	N	A	R	O	Y	D	K
N	E	Z	E	E	L	P	P	A	B	A	R	C	K	I
I	A	I	B	L	A	C	K	B	E	R	R	Y	Y	G
R	P	V	E	M	G	R	A	P	E	F	R	U	I	T
E	P	S	S	I	Y	H	Y	B	P	R	U	N	E	G
G	L	A	O	P	Y	R	R	E	B	E	U	L	B	A
N	E	V	O	U	B	E	R	D	H	Y	H	T	J	G
A	L	O	G	A	D	S	E	E	P	D	N	S	L	R
T	Y	C	N	L	I	R	H	U	B	A	R	B	W	C
O	M	A	E	M	R	H	C	U	A	L	V	N	P	B
A	N	D	M	A	N	D	A	R	I	N	U	F	I	S
A	C	O	C	O	N	U	T	T	A	U	Q	M	U	K
P	N	C	R	P	S	S	I	B	D	L	L	Y	I	Z

Avocado
Banana
Blackberry
Blueberry
Cherry
Coconut
Crab-apple
Cranberry
Elderberry
Gooseberry
Grapefruit
Kumquat
Mandarin
Mulberry
Nectarine
Persimmon
Pineapple
Prune
Rhubarb
Tangerine

Furniture

```
K A D Q E C O U C H C I T P R
R S S R O R R I M U X S P G T
S R E W A R D F O T S E H C F
W T Q D W O L L I P Q H E D L
G X T N G R B X Y T W U I C U
D X O L E N A P A O U E A O M
D S N A X A I B U C B N L E N
I N T X U M L T P C D L L T F
W M A N T E L P I E C E L P I
Z I H T L N B R L R D R O A T
L T W A S T I A Q O W R T A T
L R M A Q P B I S E T T E E I
P P H T J R M A X K A Y Y E N
T E P R A C M A L X E M K W G
Q D F Z X A O R L O O T S G S
```

Basket
Candelabra
Carpet
Chest of drawers
Couch
Cupboard
Cushion
Fittings
Lampstand
Mantelpiece
Mirror
Ornament
Panel
Pillow
Settee
Stool
Table lamp
Tallboy
Whatnot
Writing desk

Getting an Education

C	A	M	P	U	S	E	Y	T	P	P	L	U	S	D
M	T	M	O	T	R	O	P	E	R	O	J	A	M	U
T	A	O	A	N	S	P	U	P	I	L	C	B	Q	N
Z	U	O	R	R	I	Q	O	T	M	H	J	R	A	C
X	O	R	P	O	S	T	G	R	A	D	U	A	T	E
J	Q	S	O	I	E	T	O	L	R	D	L	L	L	E
B	S	S	P	T	H	L	K	R	Y	I	A	O	T	V
W	G	A	P	R	C	S	C	U	G	S	L	H	U	H
E	T	L	S	I	I	E	W	A	L	C	S	C	S	R
L	O	C	T	M	M	Z	P	O	P	I	C	S	F	O
W	L	S	L	E	L	F	E	S	L	P	A	R	J	M
Z	X	O	T	S	N	C	S	T	N	L	I	N	E	S
L	N	O	I	T	I	U	T	L	L	I	E	J	V	I
U	P	A	P	E	R	I	J	I	F	N	A	F	A	C
B	V	D	A	R	Y	O	B	D	A	E	H	L	N	U

Campus
Chalk
Classroom
Discipline
Dunce
Fellowship
Head boy
Inspector
Lines
Major

Monitor
Paper
Postgraduate
Primary
Prize
Pupil
Report
Scholar
Trimester
Tuition

Dance and Ballet

C	I	J	E	O	U	I	U	D	S	S	D	C	U	Y
S	C	A	R	B	A	S	P	O	L	K	A	B	G	H
V	X	O	P	L	I	H	E	B	P	B	N	L	Z	F
X	P	N	N	V	A	U	R	M	R	P	S	J	S	Z
M	Z	E	P	G	R	F	H	I	U	B	E	O	K	A
A	P	P	I	A	A	F	O	L	E	R	U	M	B	A
L	E	R	R	A	B	L	I	B	S	W	R	B	G	S
O	Z	T	O	L	E	E	O	A	E	H	T	L	J	D
V	G	L	U	L	S	P	H	R	K	G	I	V	M	F
A	L	S	E	T	Q	K	L	N	C	S	U	M	J	X
T	G	U	T	H	U	R	E	D	S	A	A	I	M	W
U	N	O	T	S	E	L	R	A	H	C	Z	E	N	Y
T	S	Y	E	T	D	T	D	N	R	R	L	I	J	E
I	V	Q	Q	J	F	E	M	C	A	N	C	A	N	S
G	P	J	G	J	I	T	T	E	R	B	U	G	U	L

Arabesque
Barn dance
Barre
Bebop
Beguine
Cabriole
Cancan
Charleston
Conga
Danseur

Glissade
Jitterbug
Limbo
Pirouette
Polka
Rumba
Salsa
Shimmy
Shuffle
Tutu

Coins and Currency

R	I	G	P	B	I	M	I	Y	W	T	X	L	B	K
S	A	E	T	I	H	T	S	O	T	T	C	I	O	U
M	O	O	L	A	I	U	T	O	N	I	B	L	H	U
S	O	R	L	N	R	W	U	N	A	J	Y	S	M	R
Y	N	G	Q	L	I	E	L	B	U	O	R	C	F	T
E	G	E	P	V	Q	X	T	U	Y	P	E	S	O	L
G	I	N	N	E	F	P	C	R	O	W	N	A	F	R
X	E	O	I	L	X	P	E	E	A	Q	D	N	T	I
F	R	B	E	L	B	T	E	P	R	U	P	I	A	H
S	E	L	K	N	R	A	P	P	R	E	Q	C	M	A
U	V	E	K	C	E	E	Q	O	R	T	Y	K	S	E
V	O	D	D	I	E	U	T	C	S	Z	U	E	O	K
S	S	Y	O	I	I	P	M	S	D	A	S	L	N	F
Q	Q	S	K	D	N	U	O	P	A	L	A	D	L	S
R	U	Z	L	O	U	D	E	C	N	E	R	O	L	F

Copeck
Copper
Crown
Dime
Easterling
Florence
George noble
Moola
Nickel
Peso
Pfennig
Pound
Punt
Quarter
Quetzale
Quid
Rouble
Rupiah
Sovereign
Yuan

The Ancient World

L	K	V	A	D	E	C	D	L	D	X	U	C	U	P
P	C	E	X	F	O	H	O	N	O	R	I	U	S	L
L	A	A	R	E	N	C	P	O	M	P	E	Y	F	U
F	T	B	L	P	R	E	S	U	I	R	E	B	I	T
P	I	K	T	I	Y	X	R	F	T	H	I	Q	T	A
H	T	N	S	E	G	E	E	V	I	A	E	S	A	R
I	U	A	A	C	V	U	K	S	A	D	B	U	U	C
L	S	L	R	N	G	A	L	G	N	R	G	S	J	H
I	U	O	N	E	R	O	T	A	C	I	T	U	S	E
P	T	C	N	R	D	G	A	L	B	A	A	A	I	X
P	S	I	O	E	L	F	U	L	S	N	T	G	O	I
U	U	R	E	T	P	S	X	U	C	Y	J	A	P	B
S	G	G	Q	R	M	R	T	S	O	Q	B	A	A	L
A	U	A	L	K	R	W	S	A	S	R	P	Q	M	T
N	A	J	A	R	T	I	A	B	N	T	H	L	R	U

Agricola
Augustus
Caligula
Domitian
Eugenius
Galba
Gallus
Hadrian
Honorius
Nero
Nerva
Philippus
Plutarch
Pompey
Tacitus
Terence
Tiberius
Titus
Trajan
Xerxes

Agriculture

I	F	X	T	E	H	R	E	F	I	E	H	O	W	S
U	T	B	D	R	A	Y	E	N	I	V	N	I	A	R
N	T	E	F	E	R	T	I	L	I	Z	E	R	S	L
L	R	P	T	H	V	C	M	B	L	S	A	M	X	S
F	U	I	N	S	E	C	T	I	C	I	D	E	Y	T
I	W	P	O	E	S	P	W	S	R	R	T	I	U	R
T	R	U	I	R	T	E	A	F	O	Y	O	B	S	A
A	L	E	T	H	I	J	G	S	A	P	E	P	X	W
W	H	E	A	T	N	U	O	S	T	R	M	A	S	T
A	U	S	V	T	G	K	N	K	I	U	M	O	P	B
R	U	V	I	T	I	C	U	L	T	U	R	E	C	A
Q	R	T	T	C	D	C	O	M	B	I	N	E	R	A
C	H	A	L	R	K	R	S	I	M	R	T	F	G	U
E	U	U	U	P	A	L	A	S	N	I	Q	Z	D	K
A	R	E	C	H	W	O	E	A	E	S	E	P	T	V

Combine
Compost
Crops
Cultivation
Farmer
Fertilizer
Harvesting
Heifer
Insecticide
Pasture
Sickle
Straw
Thresher
Tiller
Tithe
Tuber
Vineyard
Viticulture
Wagon
Wheat

Changing Shape

O	M	E	T	N	H	E	N	A	G	O	N	U	L	S
P	V	R	L	O	T	F	A	W	O	C	P	K	A	I
Q	C	N	O	G	A	T	N	E	P	T	S	U	I	E
S	U	I	O	Y	N	H	E	P	T	A	G	O	N	C
I	T	C	K	L	M	A	G	L	A	G	Z	R	M	R
N	T	O	D	O	M	H	T	N	G	O	K	E	S	E
E	S	S	K	P	U	M	R	C	U	N	L	A	Q	S
Q	U	A	D	R	I	L	A	T	E	R	A	L	U	C
H	B	G	T	Y	Z	H	P	J	P	R	I	I	A	E
E	M	O	L	S	E	S	E	J	O	R	T	R	R	N
K	O	N	P	X	P	K	Z	G	L	V	P	R	E	T
U	H	Q	A	H	A	D	O	D	E	C	A	G	O	N
S	R	G	E	N	R	C	I	R	C	L	E	L	O	T
A	O	R	K	I	T	E	D	Y	V	M	H	P	Z	T
N	E	Y	X	K	M	U	D	N	P	R	A	S	T	E

Circle
Crescent
Dodecagon
Henagon
Heptagon
Hexagon
Icosagon
Kite
Octagon
Oval
Pentagon
Polygon
Quadrilateral
Rectangle
Rhombus
Sphere
Square
Trapezium
Trapezoid
Triangle

Stars of Baseball

K	D	A	L	E	M	U	R	P	H	Y	H	P	O	F
J	A	N	S	R	E	N	K	C	U	B	L	L	I	B
I	R	G	D	U	K	E	S	N	I	D	E	R	L	F
M	R	E	J	R	E	S	I	E	R	E	T	E	P	Q
M	Y	L	G	S	S	A	F	X	H	E	O	D	R	T
O	L	B	R	I	H	E	N	R	Y	A	A	R	O	N
R	K	E	J	S	A	M	O	H	T	K	N	A	R	F
R	I	R	S	Y	N	P	T	L	L	E	B	B	U	H
I	L	R	S	N	I	L	L	O	C	E	I	D	D	E
S	E	O	J	H	T	U	R	E	B	A	B	Y	O	L
F	R	A	S	E	C	R	A	G	H	C	I	R	S	I
R	K	A	S	U	I	S	C	B	E	C	C	T	A	E
A	L	K	A	L	I	N	E	C	Q	Z	T	U	T	N
J	I	C	O	R	B	S	E	H	C	K	C	A	J	B
R	E	B	U	R	G	A	D	D	I	E	J	O	S	S

Addie Joss
Al Kaline
Angel Berroa
Autry
Babe Ruth
Bill Buckner
Carlton Fisk
Dale Murphy
Darryl Kile
Duke Snider

Eddie Collins
Frank Thomas
Gruber
Henry Aaron
Hubbell
Jack Chesbro
Jim Morris
Pete Reiser
Rich Garces
Satchel Paige

Fascinating Physics

W L L S J O A M P L I T U D E
K P H B I G B A N G Y O R I C
T A C T F B I G U D T N G W R
S R N L H D H N L Y I T R G O
E T U E M N Y E W N V S S M F
P I R M U M O T D A I Y B L G
D C C I T S M I I M T L U S R
P L G S N E R S T I A X O M A
T E I S A G N M V C L X N I V
P S B I U B T E K O E S U G I
L N O O Q D C H R U R V V T T
E O T N B T O B E G A I N V Y
R T K J O L I S A O Y A S O Z
P X L R E T T A M K R A D I C
U H S T R E N T R O P Y I K I

Amplitude
Big Bang
Big Crunch
Black Hole
Convection
Dark Matter
Dynamic
Emission
Energy
Entropy
Fluid
Flux
Force
Gravity
Magnetism
Particles
Quantum
Relativity
String Theory
Vectors

Gramatically Speaking

B H A R T I C L E V I S S A P
Y O F H P A R G I D T H A A B
J G G A W V F K E T L D O Z S
P D D I P H T H O N G D C R L
A E I D I L T O M O Y E O E R
P R M E P N O M I N A T I V E
C I P C Y T R O W C I C A I F
L V E L P L U P E R F E C T L
A A R A E N O H P O L L A A E
U T A R V D U O P S I F O L X
S I T A C O G N A T E N R B I
E V I T A D H O C T L I S A V
Q E V I T A S U C C A R Q A E
C P E V I T I S N A R T N I R
H L B E V I T A C I D N I B J

Ablative
Accusative
Allophone
Article
Clause
Cognate
Dative
Declarative
Derivative
Digraph
Diphthong
Homophonous
Imperative
Indicative
Inflected
Intransitive
Nominative
Passive
Pluperfect
Reflexive

Losing Weight

E L I R S Q Z W S D X L A L F
P P C R S V I R L S A S R R M
A U A G N I L C Y C Y E R R F
U G L N Z S C I B O R E A J Y
H N O I T A T P M E T S U O I
O I R M R V E E S L A O G R D
O P I M G E S I G S H A W I X
D A E I T E S I C R E X E T D
I H S W R T T K L E A S I P I
E S A S A J Q X O H L T G P Q
T P G N I T A E W S T H H Q U
I B C G N I D I R R H N T R B
N E S L I M M I N G Y K S S W
G N I N N U R H T H V O S C U
R G N I G G O J Z R D W T D R

Aerobics
Calories
Cycling
Dieting
Exercise
Goals
Healthy
Jogging
Resistance
Riding
Running
Shaping Up
Slimming
Sweating
Swimming
Targets
Temptation
Training
Weights
Yoga

On Foot...

T	P	E	E	P	T	O	E	M	T	S	S	R	S	E
Y	A	N	S	R	E	N	I	A	R	T	Z	S	K	T
A	S	T	P	A	S	A	N	S	U	O	I	L	S	K
P	Y	P	A	X	D	O	L	T	O	O	P	A	Q	A
Q	L	U	D	W	T	A	E	E	C	B	P	D	A	G
E	L	Q	R	N	I	S	A	C	C	O	M	N	K	M
T	E	O	I	B	I	G	T	T	E	L	L	A	B	H
R	W	A	L	K	I	N	G	S	H	O	E	S	B	P
S	P	O	L	F	P	I	L	F	P	R	X	L	Y	U
G	O	O	E	R	B	K	M	F	J	U	R	M	U	R
O	N	C	I	I	R	C	T	W	A	V	D	Z	I	M
L	Z	I	K	L	L	O	S	M	I	L	P	L	C	A
C	O	T	D	S	Y	T	O	V	H	U	E	R	O	T
R	E	P	P	I	L	S	N	E	A	K	E	R	O	H
S	J	H	F	I	R	M	U	S	Y	E	O	M	P	L

Ballet
Boots
Clogs
Court
Espadrille
Flip-flop
Hold-ups
Moccasin
Mule
Peep Toe
Plimsoll
Riding
Sandals
Slipper
Sneaker
Socks
Stockings
Trainers
Walking Shoes
Welly

Pieces of Eight!

P	T	S	S	E	L	H	T	U	R	T	S	R	T	A
G	L	Z	G	E	Z	A	E	T	A	G	P	U	R	Q
S	R	N	I	A	T	P	A	C	N	G	E	D	T	F
X	Y	I	H	M	R	I	O	U	S	W	A	G	U	K
X	L	W	O	M	E	R	R	E	V	L	I	S	E	I
U	L	D	S	O	G	A	I	L	V	Y	O	V	P	D
J	O	O	T	S	O	T	L	T	G	I	U	Y	J	N
U	P	R	A	N	R	E	Y	E	P	A	T	C	H	A
E	Y	I	G	A	Y	S	R	E	N	O	S	I	R	P
Z	T	C	E	R	L	H	P	O	B	S	T	O	P	M
T	T	H	S	G	L	I	P	D	R	O	P	V	T	U
E	E	E	F	G	O	P	K	A	L	P	U	U	P	T
M	R	S	P	O	J	L	O	L	V	O	S	N	P	I
Z	P	I	E	C	E	S	O	F	E	I	G	H	T	N
K	I	W	A	L	K	T	H	E	P	L	A	N	K	Y

Bounty
Captain
Eye Patch
Gold
Hook
Hostages
Jolly Roger
Kidnap
Me Hearties
Mutiny

Pieces Of Eight
Pirate Ship
Pretty Polly
Prisoners
Ransom
Riches
Ruthless
Silver
Swag
Walk The Plank

Varieties of Cheese

W	R	R	M	A	O	N	S	U	P	M	G	S	H	Z
B	N	A	U	R	S	B	D	E	T	A	R	G	A	H
Q	B	L	U	E	T	L	Z	G	A	D	U	O	G	E
M	A	L	W	Y	I	N	G	R	P	E	Y	A	F	U
X	W	E	N	S	L	E	Y	D	A	L	E	A	Q	T
E	I	R	B	C	T	L	K	X	A	G	R	E	E	K
B	R	A	A	K	O	E	I	C	O	M	E	M	V	C
R	P	Z	A	D	N	I	S	H	H	A	D	M	H	K
I	A	Z	T	M	D	C	T	O	P	A	R	E	I	M
C	N	O	P	R	U	E	U	I	X	R	S	N	T	X
O	E	M	A	G	G	S	H	E	E	H	E	T	P	Q
T	E	I	P	U	E	T	I	C	I	Y	L	A	G	M
T	R	O	F	U	A	E	B	R	S	U	E	L	C	I
A	T	E	L	J	T	R	E	B	M	E	M	A	C	F
A	N	J	L	J	O	F	U	J	W	P	M	S	T	E

Beaufort
Blue
Brie
Caerphilly
Camembert
Cheddar
Cheshire
Edam
Emmental
Farmhouse
Gouda
Grated
Greek
Gruyere
Leicester
Mozzarella
Paneer
Ricotta
Stilton
Wensleydale

Answers

2	7	4	8	9	5	6	1	3
8	5	6	1	7	3	9	4	2
9	3	1	2	6	4	8	7	5
3	1	8	7	4	9	5	2	6
7	9	2	5	8	6	4	3	1
6	4	5	3	2	1	7	9	8
4	8	7	6	3	2	1	5	9
1	2	9	4	5	8	3	6	7
5	6	3	9	1	7	2	8	4

1

5	1	3	7	8	4	6	2	9
9	8	2	3	5	6	1	7	4
6	7	4	1	9	2	8	5	3
2	5	7	4	3	8	9	6	1
3	6	1	9	7	5	4	8	2
4	9	8	6	2	1	5	3	7
7	4	9	8	6	3	2	1	5
8	3	5	2	1	9	7	4	6
1	2	6	5	4	7	3	9	8

2

6	2	7	9	8	5	4	3	1
5	4	1	6	7	3	8	9	2
9	3	8	4	2	1	7	6	5
1	7	2	8	4	9	3	5	6
4	9	3	1	5	6	2	7	8
8	6	5	7	3	2	1	4	9
2	5	9	3	1	4	6	8	7
3	8	6	2	9	7	5	1	4
7	1	4	5	6	8	9	2	3

3

2	6	5	7	3	1	8	4	9
4	1	9	8	6	5	2	3	7
8	7	3	4	2	9	5	1	6
9	8	2	6	1	3	7	5	4
7	5	4	2	9	8	1	6	3
6	3	1	5	7	4	9	8	2
1	4	7	9	5	6	3	2	8
5	9	6	3	8	2	4	7	1
3	2	8	1	4	7	6	9	5

4

5	6	3	1	2	8	7	4	9
1	4	7	5	6	9	3	2	8
8	2	9	7	3	4	6	1	5
4	7	8	2	1	3	5	9	6
3	5	2	4	9	6	8	7	1
9	1	6	8	7	5	2	3	4
7	9	5	6	4	2	1	8	3
6	3	1	9	8	7	4	5	2
2	8	4	3	5	1	9	6	7

5

4	8	5	3	1	6	2	9	7
9	1	6	8	7	2	4	5	3
3	2	7	4	9	5	6	1	8
1	6	2	5	4	8	7	3	9
7	5	4	1	3	9	8	2	6
8	9	3	2	6	7	5	4	1
6	3	9	7	2	4	1	8	5
5	4	1	6	8	3	9	7	2
2	7	8	9	5	1	3	6	4

6

Answers

7	2	3	1	4	9	5	8	6
6	4	9	2	5	8	7	1	3
5	8	1	7	3	6	2	4	9
4	5	6	3	1	7	8	9	2
9	1	2	5	8	4	3	6	7
3	7	8	6	9	2	1	5	4
8	3	7	9	6	5	4	2	1
1	9	5	4	2	3	6	7	8
2	6	4	8	7	1	9	3	5

7

2	7	9	5	4	8	6	1	3
1	6	5	7	9	3	2	8	4
4	8	3	2	1	6	9	7	5
7	1	2	9	6	5	4	3	8
9	3	6	8	7	4	5	2	1
8	5	4	1	3	2	7	6	9
3	2	8	6	5	9	1	4	7
5	4	1	3	2	7	8	9	6
6	9	7	4	8	1	3	5	2

8

5	8	2	4	7	1	9	3	6
6	9	4	3	2	5	1	7	8
1	3	7	8	6	9	4	2	5
2	6	5	7	8	4	3	1	9
3	7	8	9	1	2	5	6	4
4	1	9	6	5	3	2	8	7
7	5	3	1	9	8	6	4	2
9	4	6	2	3	7	8	5	1
8	2	1	5	4	6	7	9	3

9

3	2	5	4	9	1	8	6	7
9	7	4	2	8	6	3	1	5
8	6	1	5	7	3	9	4	2
2	9	6	3	5	4	7	8	1
7	1	3	9	6	8	5	2	4
4	5	8	7	1	2	6	3	9
1	3	9	6	2	5	4	7	8
5	4	2	8	3	7	1	9	6
6	8	7	1	4	9	2	5	3

10

2	4	1	9	6	7	8	3	5
8	5	9	1	2	3	7	4	6
7	3	6	5	8	4	2	1	9
9	8	7	3	5	2	4	6	1
3	1	4	6	9	8	5	2	7
6	2	5	7	4	1	9	8	3
5	7	2	4	1	6	3	9	8
1	9	8	2	3	5	6	7	4
4	6	3	8	7	9	1	5	2

11

2	1	3	7	9	4	6	8	5
5	9	8	6	2	3	7	4	1
4	6	7	1	8	5	2	9	3
1	5	2	8	3	9	4	6	7
8	3	4	5	6	7	1	2	9
9	7	6	2	4	1	3	5	8
7	8	5	4	1	2	9	3	6
3	4	1	9	5	6	8	7	2
6	2	9	3	7	8	5	1	4

12

Answers

3	5	7	2	8	4	9	1	6
2	6	4	9	3	1	8	5	7
8	1	9	7	6	5	4	2	3
9	8	3	5	4	7	1	6	2
5	7	6	1	2	8	3	9	4
4	2	1	3	9	6	5	7	8
1	9	2	4	7	3	6	8	5
6	3	5	8	1	2	7	4	9
7	4	8	6	5	9	2	3	1

13

6	3	9	1	2	4	8	5	7
7	2	1	3	8	5	4	6	9
8	4	5	6	9	7	1	2	3
2	6	7	4	3	9	5	1	8
5	9	3	2	1	8	6	7	4
4	1	8	7	5	6	3	9	2
1	8	6	9	4	2	7	3	5
9	7	4	5	6	3	2	8	1
3	5	2	8	7	1	9	4	6

14

3	6	4	5	7	9	2	1	8
9	8	7	3	2	1	4	5	6
5	1	2	6	4	8	7	9	3
6	5	9	7	8	2	3	4	1
2	4	1	9	6	3	8	7	5
7	3	8	1	5	4	9	6	2
4	2	5	8	1	7	6	3	9
8	9	6	4	3	5	1	2	7
1	7	3	2	9	6	5	8	4

15

1	9	8	5	6	7	3	2	4
4	6	3	9	1	2	8	7	5
7	2	5	8	4	3	6	1	9
8	1	9	3	5	6	7	4	2
3	5	7	4	2	9	1	8	6
6	4	2	1	7	8	5	9	3
5	8	4	2	3	1	9	6	7
2	7	1	6	9	5	4	3	8
9	3	6	7	8	4	2	5	1

16

9	2	6	8	1	7	5	4	3
1	4	5	6	2	3	7	9	8
3	8	7	9	4	5	6	1	2
8	7	9	1	3	2	4	5	6
6	3	4	7	5	9	2	8	1
5	1	2	4	8	6	9	3	7
2	9	8	3	6	4	1	7	5
4	6	3	5	7	1	8	2	9
7	5	1	2	9	8	3	6	4

17

1	5	3	8	4	9	2	6	7
4	8	6	7	5	2	9	3	1
9	7	2	6	1	3	4	8	5
7	2	1	3	6	4	5	9	8
3	9	5	1	8	7	6	4	2
6	4	8	2	9	5	1	7	3
2	1	9	4	7	8	3	5	6
8	3	4	5	2	6	7	1	9
5	6	7	9	3	1	8	2	4

18

Answers

7	3	5	8	1	4	6	2	9
2	1	4	3	6	9	7	5	8
8	9	6	7	2	5	1	4	3
9	8	2	5	3	6	4	1	7
5	4	7	1	8	2	3	9	6
3	6	1	4	9	7	2	8	5
1	7	3	9	4	8	5	6	2
4	2	9	6	5	3	8	7	1
6	5	8	2	7	1	9	3	4

19

1	6	2	9	3	8	4	7	5
5	8	9	6	7	4	1	2	3
4	3	7	1	2	5	6	8	9
7	9	8	5	6	1	3	4	2
2	4	1	7	8	3	9	5	6
6	5	3	2	4	9	8	1	7
9	1	4	3	5	2	7	6	8
3	7	5	8	1	6	2	9	4
8	2	6	4	9	7	5	3	1

20

8	4	3	6	5	2	9	7	1
5	6	2	7	9	1	4	8	3
7	1	9	4	8	3	2	5	6
6	5	1	2	4	8	3	9	7
4	2	8	3	7	9	6	1	5
9	3	7	1	6	5	8	2	4
2	7	5	8	3	6	1	4	9
3	8	4	9	1	7	5	6	2
1	9	6	5	2	4	7	3	8

21

1	9	7	6	3	8	5	2	4
6	2	5	1	9	4	3	8	7
3	4	8	5	2	7	9	6	1
9	8	3	4	1	5	2	7	6
5	1	2	7	6	9	4	3	8
7	6	4	2	8	3	1	9	5
8	3	6	9	4	1	7	5	2
2	7	1	3	5	6	8	4	9
4	5	9	8	7	2	6	1	3

22

8	3	6	4	5	1	7	9	2
7	1	9	6	8	2	3	4	5
4	5	2	7	9	3	1	8	6
6	4	5	9	7	8	2	3	1
2	8	7	1	3	5	9	6	4
1	9	3	2	4	6	5	7	8
5	7	8	3	1	4	6	2	9
9	2	1	8	6	7	4	5	3
3	6	4	5	2	9	8	1	7

23

8	9	7	3	5	1	2	4	6
2	6	5	7	9	4	8	3	1
1	3	4	2	8	6	7	9	5
6	8	3	5	1	7	9	2	4
4	5	2	8	3	9	1	6	7
9	7	1	6	4	2	5	8	3
3	1	6	9	7	8	4	5	2
7	2	8	4	6	5	3	1	9
5	4	9	1	2	3	6	7	8

24

Answers

9	8	5	7	1	4	2	6	3
1	7	6	5	2	3	8	4	9
4	2	3	8	9	6	1	7	5
7	6	4	3	8	1	9	5	2
8	9	2	6	7	5	4	3	1
5	3	1	2	4	9	7	8	6
2	5	9	4	3	7	6	1	8
3	4	8	1	6	2	5	9	7
6	1	7	9	5	8	3	2	4

25

9	4	8	6	5	3	1	7	2
1	7	5	8	9	2	4	3	6
6	2	3	1	4	7	9	8	5
7	6	9	4	1	8	2	5	3
3	8	4	9	2	5	6	1	7
2	5	1	3	7	6	8	4	9
8	1	2	7	3	9	5	6	4
5	3	6	2	8	4	7	9	1
4	9	7	5	6	1	3	2	8

26

7	2	8	3	4	5	6	9	1
1	9	5	7	2	6	4	3	8
6	3	4	8	1	9	5	2	7
4	1	6	5	3	7	2	8	9
9	7	3	6	8	2	1	5	4
5	8	2	4	9	1	3	7	6
3	5	9	1	6	8	7	4	2
2	6	7	9	5	4	8	1	3
8	4	1	2	7	3	9	6	5

27

6	3	8	1	5	4	9	2	7
9	4	2	7	3	8	5	6	1
1	7	5	9	2	6	8	3	4
2	5	1	6	9	3	7	4	8
3	8	7	2	4	1	6	5	9
4	6	9	8	7	5	3	1	2
5	1	3	4	8	7	2	9	6
7	9	4	5	6	2	1	8	3
8	2	6	3	1	9	4	7	5

28

9	6	4	1	2	8	5	3	7
1	3	2	9	5	7	4	6	8
7	5	8	6	3	4	9	1	2
2	9	3	5	6	1	8	7	4
5	1	7	4	8	9	3	2	6
4	8	6	2	7	3	1	9	5
3	4	5	7	1	2	6	8	9
8	2	9	3	4	6	7	5	1
6	7	1	8	9	5	2	4	3

29

1	2	3	6	8	4	5	9	7
6	4	8	9	5	7	2	3	1
7	9	5	2	1	3	8	4	6
3	6	9	1	2	5	4	7	8
4	5	1	3	7	8	9	6	2
8	7	2	4	9	6	1	5	3
9	8	7	5	6	1	3	2	4
5	3	6	8	4	2	7	1	9
2	1	4	7	3	9	6	8	5

30

Answers

3	5	4	8	7	9	2	6	1
1	8	2	5	4	6	3	9	7
6	9	7	1	3	2	4	5	8
4	2	9	7	8	1	5	3	6
8	6	5	2	9	3	1	7	4
7	1	3	4	6	5	9	8	2
2	7	1	3	5	8	6	4	9
5	4	6	9	1	7	8	2	3
9	3	8	6	2	4	7	1	5

31

3	4	8	5	6	7	1	9	2
7	5	2	4	9	1	3	8	6
6	9	1	8	2	3	5	7	4
1	3	5	2	8	9	6	4	7
2	6	9	3	7	4	8	5	1
8	7	4	6	1	5	9	2	3
4	8	7	9	3	6	2	1	5
5	2	3	1	4	8	7	6	9
9	1	6	7	5	2	4	3	8

32

2	3	7	1	9	4	8	6	5
9	5	6	2	7	8	1	3	4
1	8	4	5	3	6	9	7	2
5	2	3	4	8	1	6	9	7
4	9	8	7	6	2	3	5	1
7	6	1	3	5	9	2	4	8
3	1	2	9	4	7	5	8	6
8	7	9	6	2	5	4	1	3
6	4	5	8	1	3	7	2	9

33

5	7	6	9	8	4	3	1	2
4	8	2	7	3	1	9	5	6
9	1	3	2	5	6	4	8	7
2	5	9	8	4	3	6	7	1
6	3	7	5	1	9	2	4	8
1	4	8	6	7	2	5	9	3
8	6	1	3	9	5	7	2	4
7	2	5	4	6	8	1	3	9
3	9	4	1	2	7	8	6	5

34

8	5	1	7	4	2	9	6	3
6	4	2	5	9	3	8	1	7
7	3	9	6	1	8	5	4	2
5	6	8	2	7	9	4	3	1
3	9	4	1	5	6	2	7	8
1	2	7	3	8	4	6	5	9
2	1	5	8	6	7	3	9	4
9	8	6	4	3	1	7	2	5
4	7	3	9	2	5	1	8	6

35

1	6	7	9	3	8	2	4	5
8	5	3	6	2	4	9	1	7
2	9	4	7	1	5	8	3	6
5	2	8	4	6	3	1	7	9
9	3	6	8	7	1	4	5	2
7	4	1	2	5	9	3	6	8
6	8	5	3	4	2	7	9	1
4	1	2	5	9	7	6	8	3
3	7	9	1	8	6	5	2	4

36

Answers

9	1	7	5	8	3	2	6	4
3	5	2	6	4	7	8	1	9
6	8	4	1	9	2	7	5	3
8	7	5	4	6	1	9	3	2
4	2	9	7	3	5	6	8	1
1	3	6	9	2	8	4	7	5
2	6	3	8	1	4	5	9	7
7	4	8	3	5	9	1	2	6
5	9	1	2	7	6	3	4	8

37

7	5	8	6	4	3	9	1	2
2	3	6	7	1	9	5	8	4
9	1	4	5	8	2	3	6	7
4	7	5	3	9	8	6	2	1
1	8	3	2	6	4	7	5	9
6	9	2	1	7	5	8	4	3
8	6	7	9	2	1	4	3	5
3	2	9	4	5	6	1	7	8
5	4	1	8	3	7	2	9	6

38

7	8	6	1	2	3	9	5	4
9	5	4	7	6	8	1	2	3
3	2	1	9	4	5	7	6	8
8	6	3	5	9	2	4	1	7
4	9	2	8	7	1	5	3	6
1	7	5	6	3	4	8	9	2
6	1	8	2	5	7	3	4	9
2	4	7	3	1	9	6	8	5
5	3	9	4	8	6	2	7	1

39

3	1	9	4	6	5	7	2	8
8	7	4	3	2	9	1	6	5
5	2	6	7	8	1	9	4	3
2	8	7	1	3	4	6	5	9
6	5	1	9	7	2	8	3	4
9	4	3	8	5	6	2	7	1
1	3	5	6	9	7	4	8	2
4	6	8	2	1	3	5	9	7
7	9	2	5	4	8	3	1	6

40

3	8	7	1	2	5	4	9	6
4	1	2	9	6	7	8	3	5
5	9	6	4	3	8	7	1	2
2	3	4	7	9	6	1	5	8
1	5	9	8	4	3	6	2	7
6	7	8	5	1	2	9	4	3
9	2	5	6	8	4	3	7	1
7	6	1	3	5	9	2	8	4
8	4	3	2	7	1	5	6	9

41

5	6	4	2	1	7	9	3	8
9	8	3	4	5	6	2	7	1
1	2	7	8	9	3	5	6	4
8	9	6	7	3	4	1	5	2
4	7	5	1	8	2	3	9	6
2	3	1	9	6	5	4	8	7
6	5	2	3	7	1	8	4	9
3	4	9	6	2	8	7	1	5
7	1	8	5	4	9	6	2	3

42

Answers

3	1	9	2	5	8	4	7	6
2	7	4	3	9	6	1	8	5
5	8	6	1	7	4	3	2	9
6	3	1	9	4	2	8	5	7
4	9	7	5	8	1	2	6	3
8	2	5	6	3	7	9	1	4
1	5	2	4	6	9	7	3	8
9	6	8	7	2	3	5	4	1
7	4	3	8	1	5	6	9	2

43

2	9	8	1	5	7	6	4	3
6	7	5	3	4	9	1	2	8
3	1	4	2	8	6	7	5	9
4	2	7	8	9	5	3	1	6
5	8	1	6	3	2	4	9	7
9	3	6	4	7	1	2	8	5
8	6	9	7	1	4	5	3	2
1	5	2	9	6	3	8	7	4
7	4	3	5	2	8	9	6	1

44

6	4	1	7	5	3	9	8	2
8	9	5	2	4	1	7	6	3
3	7	2	9	8	6	4	1	5
2	8	4	1	3	7	5	9	6
7	6	9	5	2	8	3	4	1
1	5	3	4	6	9	8	2	7
5	3	6	8	9	2	1	7	4
4	1	8	6	7	5	2	3	9
9	2	7	3	1	4	6	5	8

45

6	4	1	8	7	9	3	5	2
3	5	2	1	4	6	8	7	9
9	7	8	3	2	5	1	4	6
4	9	3	7	5	1	6	2	8
2	1	5	6	8	4	9	3	7
8	6	7	9	3	2	5	1	4
1	2	6	5	9	7	4	8	3
5	8	4	2	6	3	7	9	1
7	3	9	4	1	8	2	6	5

46

9	3	8	7	4	6	2	1	5
6	5	7	2	9	1	3	4	8
1	2	4	3	5	8	6	7	9
2	9	6	8	7	5	1	3	4
8	4	1	9	6	3	5	2	7
3	7	5	1	2	4	8	9	6
5	6	2	4	3	7	9	8	1
7	1	3	5	8	9	4	6	2
4	8	9	6	1	2	7	5	3

47

5	4	6	3	8	2	9	7	1
8	1	2	9	4	7	6	5	3
7	9	3	1	6	5	2	4	8
2	5	8	7	3	9	1	6	4
6	7	9	8	1	4	3	2	5
1	3	4	5	2	6	8	9	7
4	6	1	2	5	3	7	8	9
3	2	7	4	9	8	5	1	6
9	8	5	6	7	1	4	3	2

48

Answers

6	8	5	7	1	3	4	2	9
9	1	2	4	8	5	6	3	7
3	7	4	9	6	2	1	8	5
1	4	8	3	5	9	2	7	6
7	6	3	2	4	1	5	9	8
2	5	9	8	7	6	3	4	1
5	2	7	1	9	4	8	6	3
8	3	6	5	2	7	9	1	4
4	9	1	6	3	8	7	5	2

49

3	4	2	8	9	5	1	6	7
7	1	6	3	4	2	8	9	5
9	8	5	6	1	7	2	3	4
1	3	4	9	7	8	6	5	2
5	7	8	2	6	4	3	1	9
6	2	9	1	5	3	4	7	8
4	9	1	5	8	6	7	2	3
2	6	7	4	3	9	5	8	1
8	5	3	7	2	1	9	4	6

50

2	4	9	3	1	7	6	5	8
1	5	3	8	6	2	4	9	7
6	8	7	4	5	9	2	1	3
8	1	6	7	9	3	5	4	2
3	7	5	6	2	4	9	8	1
4	9	2	1	8	5	7	3	6
9	6	1	5	7	8	3	2	4
7	2	4	9	3	1	8	6	5
5	3	8	2	4	6	1	7	9

51

9	8	1	4	7	6	5	3	2
2	3	6	8	5	9	1	4	7
4	7	5	1	3	2	8	6	9
1	2	8	9	4	5	3	7	6
7	9	3	6	1	8	2	5	4
5	6	4	7	2	3	9	1	8
6	4	9	5	8	1	7	2	3
8	1	2	3	6	7	4	9	5
3	5	7	2	9	4	6	8	1

52

1	9	2	4	8	6	7	3	5
7	5	8	2	9	3	4	6	1
4	6	3	1	5	7	8	9	2
3	4	5	7	1	9	2	8	6
9	2	7	8	6	5	1	4	3
8	1	6	3	2	4	5	7	9
6	7	4	5	3	1	9	2	8
5	8	9	6	4	2	3	1	7
2	3	1	9	7	8	6	5	4

53

9	7	1	5	3	2	4	8	6
5	6	4	1	7	8	2	9	3
2	3	8	6	9	4	7	5	1
7	1	5	8	2	6	9	3	4
3	4	2	9	1	5	6	7	8
6	8	9	7	4	3	5	1	2
8	2	6	3	5	9	1	4	7
1	9	3	4	6	7	8	2	5
4	5	7	2	8	1	3	6	9

54

Answers

9	4	3	7	2	5	6	8	1
5	8	6	1	9	4	7	2	3
7	1	2	6	3	8	4	5	9
1	9	8	3	7	2	5	6	4
3	2	4	5	8	6	9	1	7
6	5	7	4	1	9	8	3	2
2	3	5	8	4	7	1	9	6
8	7	9	2	6	1	3	4	5
4	6	1	9	5	3	2	7	8

55

2	5	3	6	1	9	7	4	8
9	8	1	2	7	4	6	3	5
7	6	4	8	3	5	9	2	1
3	4	2	7	5	8	1	9	6
1	9	8	4	6	3	2	5	7
5	7	6	9	2	1	4	8	3
6	2	9	3	8	7	5	1	4
8	1	7	5	4	2	3	6	9
4	3	5	1	9	6	8	7	2

56

3	5	7	4	1	6	8	9	2
8	6	4	3	9	2	1	7	5
9	2	1	8	5	7	6	4	3
5	3	6	1	4	9	2	8	7
1	4	2	7	8	5	3	6	9
7	9	8	2	6	3	5	1	4
2	1	3	6	7	4	9	5	8
4	8	5	9	3	1	7	2	6
6	7	9	5	2	8	4	3	1

57

2	1	5	3	7	4	6	8	9
6	9	4	5	8	2	7	1	3
7	3	8	6	1	9	5	2	4
8	2	1	9	3	6	4	7	5
3	4	6	8	5	7	2	9	1
9	5	7	2	4	1	8	3	6
1	6	2	7	9	5	3	4	8
5	8	9	4	2	3	1	6	7
4	7	3	1	6	8	9	5	2

58

3	1	2	6	4	9	7	8	5
9	7	6	5	3	8	2	1	4
4	8	5	2	7	1	9	6	3
1	9	3	7	2	6	4	5	8
8	6	7	4	1	5	3	2	9
2	5	4	9	8	3	6	7	1
7	2	9	8	5	4	1	3	6
5	4	1	3	6	7	8	9	2
6	3	8	1	9	2	5	4	7

59

7	6	5	2	4	1	9	3	8
4	8	9	5	6	3	1	7	2
1	3	2	7	8	9	5	4	6
8	9	4	3	2	6	7	1	5
2	1	7	9	5	8	4	6	3
6	5	3	1	7	4	2	8	9
3	7	6	4	9	2	8	5	1
9	4	1	8	3	5	6	2	7
5	2	8	6	1	7	3	9	4

60

Answers

9	1	6	2	3	7	5	8	4
5	2	8	9	1	4	6	3	7
4	3	7	5	8	6	9	1	2
2	7	1	6	5	8	4	9	3
6	9	3	1	4	2	8	7	5
8	5	4	3	7	9	2	6	1
3	4	9	8	2	1	7	5	6
7	6	5	4	9	3	1	2	8
1	8	2	7	6	5	3	4	9

61

3	4	6	9	1	5	2	7	8
8	5	7	2	4	6	1	3	9
9	2	1	8	3	7	4	5	6
4	1	3	7	9	2	6	8	5
5	6	9	1	8	3	7	4	2
2	7	8	5	6	4	9	1	3
1	3	4	6	5	9	8	2	7
7	9	5	4	2	8	3	6	1
6	8	2	3	7	1	5	9	4

62

5	1	9	6	7	2	3	4	8
6	3	4	9	8	5	2	7	1
8	7	2	4	3	1	5	6	9
2	9	3	7	1	6	8	5	4
7	5	1	8	9	4	6	3	2
4	8	6	5	2	3	9	1	7
1	6	5	2	4	9	7	8	3
9	4	7	3	5	8	1	2	6
3	2	8	1	6	7	4	9	5

63

3	8	1	6	9	7	5	2	4
4	5	7	2	3	8	6	9	1
2	6	9	1	5	4	7	8	3
1	7	2	3	6	5	9	4	8
9	4	8	7	1	2	3	6	5
6	3	5	4	8	9	2	1	7
5	1	6	9	4	3	8	7	2
7	9	3	8	2	1	4	5	6
8	2	4	5	7	6	1	3	9

64

8	2	9	7	4	5	3	1	6
4	6	1	3	8	9	2	5	7
7	3	5	2	1	6	8	9	4
5	4	2	1	7	3	6	8	9
1	9	3	6	5	8	4	7	2
6	7	8	9	2	4	5	3	1
9	8	4	5	6	7	1	2	3
2	5	7	4	3	1	9	6	8
3	1	6	8	9	2	7	4	5

65

6	2	7	3	9	5	8	4	1
9	5	1	8	6	4	7	2	3
8	4	3	2	7	1	9	6	5
3	1	8	5	2	9	4	7	6
5	6	4	1	8	7	3	9	2
2	7	9	6	4	3	5	1	8
4	3	2	9	5	6	1	8	7
1	9	6	7	3	8	2	5	4
7	8	5	4	1	2	6	3	9

66

Answers

9	7	6	1	8	3	5	4	2
1	2	4	9	5	6	7	8	3
8	5	3	4	2	7	1	9	6
5	6	8	3	9	4	2	1	7
4	3	7	8	1	2	9	6	5
2	9	1	6	7	5	8	3	4
6	8	5	2	3	1	4	7	9
7	4	9	5	6	8	3	2	1
3	1	2	7	4	9	6	5	8

67

6	5	1	9	7	8	4	3	2
9	3	7	5	4	2	8	1	6
8	2	4	3	1	6	9	7	5
1	8	5	6	2	7	3	9	4
4	7	6	8	3	9	2	5	1
3	9	2	1	5	4	7	6	8
5	6	8	4	9	3	1	2	7
2	4	3	7	6	1	5	8	9
7	1	9	2	8	5	6	4	3

68

4	7	2	3	1	8	5	6	9
5	6	1	2	7	9	4	8	3
3	9	8	4	5	6	2	7	1
9	8	4	1	3	2	6	5	7
6	5	3	7	9	4	8	1	2
1	2	7	8	6	5	3	9	4
2	1	5	9	8	3	7	4	6
8	3	9	6	4	7	1	2	5
7	4	6	5	2	1	9	3	8

69

7	9	1	4	6	8	2	3	5
8	4	3	5	1	2	6	7	9
2	6	5	3	9	7	4	8	1
5	8	6	7	2	9	3	1	4
3	1	4	8	5	6	7	9	2
9	2	7	1	3	4	8	5	6
1	7	2	6	8	5	9	4	3
6	3	8	9	4	1	5	2	7
4	5	9	2	7	3	1	6	8

70

9	3	7	5	6	4	1	8	2
4	1	5	2	7	8	3	9	6
8	2	6	3	1	9	5	4	7
7	6	4	8	5	3	2	1	9
3	5	1	6	9	2	8	7	4
2	8	9	1	4	7	6	3	5
1	4	2	7	8	6	9	5	3
6	7	8	9	3	5	4	2	1
5	9	3	4	2	1	7	6	8

71

5	4	7	9	6	3	1	8	2
9	8	1	2	4	5	6	7	3
3	2	6	7	1	8	9	5	4
8	6	9	4	7	1	2	3	5
1	7	4	3	5	2	8	6	9
2	3	5	8	9	6	7	4	1
4	1	8	6	3	9	5	2	7
7	5	2	1	8	4	3	9	6
6	9	3	5	2	7	4	1	8

72

Answers

8	4	6	9	2	1	7	3	5
5	1	2	8	3	7	6	9	4
7	9	3	4	5	6	2	1	8
3	8	5	6	7	2	9	4	1
1	6	9	5	4	8	3	2	7
2	7	4	3	1	9	5	8	6
4	2	1	7	6	3	8	5	9
6	5	8	2	9	4	1	7	3
9	3	7	1	8	5	4	6	2

73

8	7	6	9	4	3	2	5	1
5	2	3	1	6	7	9	8	4
4	1	9	5	2	8	3	6	7
7	9	2	8	3	4	5	1	6
1	3	4	7	5	6	8	9	2
6	8	5	2	1	9	7	4	3
3	5	7	4	9	1	6	2	8
9	6	1	3	8	2	4	7	5
2	4	8	6	7	5	1	3	9

74

7	9	2	1	8	6	5	3	4
5	6	3	2	7	4	9	1	8
4	8	1	5	3	9	6	7	2
3	4	9	8	1	2	7	6	5
8	1	7	3	6	5	2	4	9
2	5	6	4	9	7	1	8	3
6	7	4	9	2	3	8	5	1
9	3	8	6	5	1	4	2	7
1	2	5	7	4	8	3	9	6

75

1	2	8	5	4	9	7	6	3
9	7	6	3	2	8	5	4	1
3	4	5	6	1	7	9	2	8
2	9	3	1	5	6	4	8	7
7	5	1	4	8	2	3	9	6
6	8	4	7	9	3	2	1	5
8	3	7	2	6	4	1	5	9
5	6	2	9	3	1	8	7	4
4	1	9	8	7	5	6	3	2

76

5	8	1	4	3	2	6	7	9
6	2	7	8	5	9	1	4	3
3	9	4	7	6	1	2	5	8
8	7	5	9	1	6	3	2	4
4	3	2	5	8	7	9	6	1
1	6	9	2	4	3	5	8	7
2	5	8	1	9	4	7	3	6
9	4	6	3	7	5	8	1	2
7	1	3	6	2	8	4	9	5

77

1	7	8	6	5	3	2	4	9
9	3	5	4	2	1	8	6	7
6	2	4	9	7	8	1	3	5
8	6	3	2	1	7	9	5	4
2	4	1	5	6	9	7	8	3
5	9	7	8	3	4	6	1	2
3	5	6	7	8	2	4	9	1
7	1	9	3	4	6	5	2	8
4	8	2	1	9	5	3	7	6

78

Answers

4	3	8	5	6	1	9	2	7
9	5	7	2	8	4	6	3	1
6	2	1	9	3	7	5	8	4
2	7	5	6	1	9	3	4	8
1	8	4	3	2	5	7	6	9
3	6	9	7	4	8	2	1	5
8	9	3	1	7	6	4	5	2
7	1	6	4	5	2	8	9	3
5	4	2	8	9	3	1	7	6

79

3	5	4	8	1	9	6	7	2
7	9	2	6	3	4	5	1	8
8	1	6	2	7	5	9	3	4
4	7	9	3	2	1	8	6	5
5	6	8	4	9	7	1	2	3
1	2	3	5	8	6	7	4	9
6	8	7	9	4	2	3	5	1
2	3	1	7	5	8	4	9	6
9	4	5	1	6	3	2	8	7

80

5	1	7	6	8	3	9	4	2
2	8	4	5	9	1	3	7	6
3	9	6	4	7	2	1	8	5
6	3	2	9	1	4	7	5	8
4	7	9	8	5	6	2	1	3
1	5	8	2	3	7	4	6	9
8	4	5	1	2	9	6	3	7
9	6	3	7	4	5	8	2	1
7	2	1	3	6	8	5	9	4

81

3	5	7	6	1	9	8	2	4
4	8	6	3	7	2	9	5	1
2	1	9	4	5	8	6	7	3
6	2	8	9	3	4	5	1	7
9	4	1	5	8	7	3	6	2
5	7	3	1	2	6	4	9	8
1	9	2	8	6	3	7	4	5
7	3	4	2	9	5	1	8	6
8	6	5	7	4	1	2	3	9

82

3	4	9	1	8	2	6	7	5
8	7	2	4	6	5	1	3	9
1	6	5	7	3	9	2	4	8
6	5	3	9	2	4	8	1	7
4	9	8	6	1	7	5	2	3
2	1	7	3	5	8	9	6	4
9	3	6	5	4	1	7	8	2
5	2	4	8	7	6	3	9	1
7	8	1	2	9	3	4	5	6

83

2	3	8	6	5	4	9	1	7
1	9	7	3	2	8	4	5	6
4	6	5	7	9	1	8	2	3
8	7	4	2	6	3	1	9	5
6	5	9	1	4	7	2	3	8
3	2	1	5	8	9	6	7	4
5	1	2	4	7	6	3	8	9
7	8	6	9	3	2	5	4	1
9	4	3	8	1	5	7	6	2

84

Answers

4	3	2	9	1	7	6	8	5
7	9	8	2	6	5	1	3	4
1	5	6	3	8	4	7	2	9
2	8	9	7	4	6	5	1	3
6	1	4	5	3	2	9	7	8
3	7	5	8	9	1	4	6	2
9	2	1	6	5	8	3	4	7
8	6	3	4	7	9	2	5	1
5	4	7	1	2	3	8	9	6

85

4	5	9	2	6	3	7	1	8
2	1	7	9	5	8	4	3	6
6	8	3	4	7	1	9	5	2
9	2	4	6	3	7	1	8	5
1	3	8	5	2	4	6	7	9
7	6	5	8	1	9	3	2	4
3	4	2	7	8	6	5	9	1
5	7	6	1	9	2	8	4	3
8	9	1	3	4	5	2	6	7

86

1	3	6	9	7	5	2	8	4
5	7	4	3	2	8	1	6	9
9	2	8	1	6	4	5	3	7
4	1	3	6	9	2	7	5	8
6	5	9	4	8	7	3	2	1
2	8	7	5	1	3	9	4	6
7	9	2	8	3	6	4	1	5
3	6	5	7	4	1	8	9	2
8	4	1	2	5	9	6	7	3

87

6	4	3	8	9	1	7	2	5
9	2	5	6	3	7	4	8	1
1	8	7	5	4	2	3	6	9
5	1	8	9	7	4	2	3	6
7	9	4	3	2	6	1	5	8
3	6	2	1	8	5	9	7	4
2	5	9	4	6	3	8	1	7
8	3	6	7	1	9	5	4	2
4	7	1	2	5	8	6	9	3

88

1	7	8	4	9	2	3	5	6
6	9	3	1	5	7	4	2	8
5	2	4	8	6	3	1	9	7
4	6	7	3	1	5	2	8	9
3	8	2	6	7	9	5	1	4
9	5	1	2	4	8	6	7	3
8	1	6	7	2	4	9	3	5
7	4	5	9	3	1	8	6	2
2	3	9	5	8	6	7	4	1

89

9	6	2	5	1	3	4	7	8
8	4	7	6	2	9	1	5	3
5	3	1	8	4	7	6	2	9
1	7	8	3	5	2	9	6	4
3	2	4	9	6	8	5	1	7
6	9	5	1	7	4	8	3	2
4	1	3	2	9	6	7	8	5
7	8	6	4	3	5	2	9	1
2	5	9	7	8	1	3	4	6

90

Answers

3	9	4	7	5	8	6	1	2
1	7	2	3	6	4	5	9	8
5	6	8	9	2	1	4	7	3
4	5	9	6	8	2	1	3	7
7	1	3	4	9	5	8	2	6
8	2	6	1	7	3	9	4	5
9	8	1	5	3	7	2	6	4
6	3	5	2	4	9	7	8	1
2	4	7	8	1	6	3	5	9

91

4	5	7	2	1	9	6	8	3
9	3	6	5	8	4	7	2	1
8	1	2	3	7	6	9	4	5
2	4	5	9	3	8	1	6	7
1	9	3	6	2	7	4	5	8
6	7	8	1	4	5	3	9	2
7	2	9	4	5	1	8	3	6
3	6	1	8	9	2	5	7	4
5	8	4	7	6	3	2	1	9

92

2	9	8	5	6	3	4	7	1
3	6	4	1	7	8	9	2	5
7	1	5	4	2	9	3	8	6
9	8	3	6	4	5	7	1	2
6	4	7	2	8	1	5	3	9
1	5	2	3	9	7	8	6	4
8	7	6	9	1	4	2	5	3
4	3	1	8	5	2	6	9	7
5	2	9	7	3	6	1	4	8

93

4	3	7	6	8	1	5	9	2
6	2	9	7	5	3	4	1	8
8	5	1	2	9	4	7	3	6
3	4	6	8	1	7	2	5	9
9	7	8	5	3	2	6	4	1
5	1	2	9	4	6	3	8	7
1	6	5	4	7	8	9	2	3
7	8	4	3	2	9	1	6	5
2	9	3	1	6	5	8	7	4

94

3	5	8	9	7	4	6	2	1
2	6	1	5	8	3	7	4	9
4	9	7	6	2	1	8	3	5
1	8	2	3	5	7	9	6	4
6	7	3	8	4	9	5	1	2
9	4	5	2	1	6	3	7	8
5	3	9	4	6	2	1	8	7
8	1	4	7	3	5	2	9	6
7	2	6	1	9	8	4	5	3

95

5	7	4	1	9	2	8	3	6
8	9	6	3	4	7	5	2	1
3	1	2	8	6	5	7	9	4
2	4	3	9	7	8	6	1	5
1	6	5	4	2	3	9	8	7
7	8	9	5	1	6	2	4	3
6	5	1	2	8	4	3	7	9
4	2	7	6	3	9	1	5	8
9	3	8	7	5	1	4	6	2

96

Answers

5	9	1	4	8	3	7	6	2
6	4	2	5	1	7	3	8	9
3	7	8	6	9	2	1	4	5
4	2	5	9	6	1	8	7	3
9	1	3	7	4	8	5	2	6
7	8	6	2	3	5	9	1	4
2	3	9	8	7	6	4	5	1
1	5	7	3	2	4	6	9	8
8	6	4	1	5	9	2	3	7

97

7	9	5	6	4	8	1	2	3
6	2	3	1	9	5	4	7	8
4	1	8	3	2	7	9	6	5
9	5	6	2	8	1	3	4	7
2	8	4	5	7	3	6	1	9
3	7	1	4	6	9	5	8	2
5	4	7	9	1	2	8	3	6
1	3	2	8	5	6	7	9	4
8	6	9	7	3	4	2	5	1

98

2	3	5	6	1	9	4	7	8
7	9	4	2	8	3	6	1	5
1	8	6	7	4	5	2	3	9
8	5	7	4	9	2	1	6	3
9	2	3	1	7	6	8	5	4
6	4	1	3	5	8	7	9	2
3	6	9	8	2	7	5	4	1
5	1	2	9	6	4	3	8	7
4	7	8	5	3	1	9	2	6

99

7	2	1	5	8	3	4	9	6
3	6	8	7	4	9	2	1	5
5	9	4	6	2	1	8	7	3
4	1	3	8	9	2	6	5	7
2	5	9	1	6	7	3	8	4
8	7	6	4	3	5	1	2	9
1	4	5	3	7	8	9	6	2
9	3	7	2	1	6	5	4	8
6	8	2	9	5	4	7	3	1

100

7	5	1	8	9	6	4	3	2
6	8	9	3	4	2	7	1	5
4	2	3	7	1	5	9	6	8
5	3	4	9	8	7	1	2	6
8	9	7	6	2	1	5	4	3
1	6	2	5	3	4	8	7	9
9	1	5	2	7	3	6	8	4
2	4	8	1	6	9	3	5	7
3	7	6	4	5	8	2	9	1

101

9	7	4	3	8	6	1	5	2
8	5	2	4	1	9	7	3	6
1	6	3	7	2	5	4	9	8
4	1	9	8	3	7	2	6	5
5	3	7	6	9	2	8	4	1
2	8	6	5	4	1	9	7	3
7	2	1	9	6	3	5	8	4
3	4	5	1	7	8	6	2	9
6	9	8	2	5	4	3	1	7

102

Answers

4	1	9	5	6	2	7	8	3
3	5	2	4	8	7	6	1	9
6	8	7	1	3	9	5	2	4
1	9	6	7	5	3	2	4	8
5	4	8	9	2	1	3	7	6
2	7	3	6	4	8	1	9	5
7	3	1	8	9	6	4	5	2
9	6	5	2	1	4	8	3	7
8	2	4	3	7	5	9	6	1

103

9	8	5	4	7	1	6	3	2
2	4	7	3	6	9	1	8	5
1	6	3	8	2	5	4	7	9
6	3	4	9	5	7	8	2	1
8	1	9	6	3	2	7	5	4
7	5	2	1	4	8	9	6	3
5	2	6	7	9	4	3	1	8
3	9	8	2	1	6	5	4	7
4	7	1	5	8	3	2	9	6

104

6	3	8	9	2	1	7	4	5
9	5	4	8	7	6	1	2	3
2	1	7	4	3	5	6	9	8
8	2	5	1	4	9	3	6	7
4	9	3	7	6	8	5	1	2
7	6	1	3	5	2	9	8	4
1	7	9	5	8	4	2	3	6
3	8	2	6	9	7	4	5	1
5	4	6	2	1	3	8	7	9

105

106

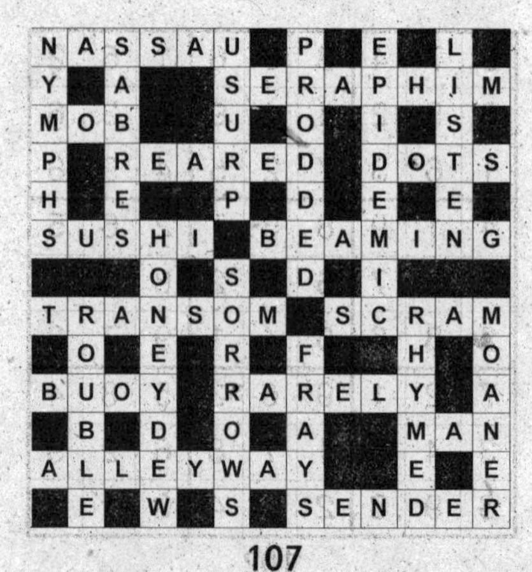

107

108

Answers

S	T	A	N	Z	A		E		A		O	
L		B			S	A	N	C	T	I	F	Y
E	M	U			S		V		O		F	
E		S	P	H	E	R	E		M	E	E	K
V		E			S		L		I		R	
E	O	S	I	N		P	O	S	S	E	S	S
			N		S		P		E			
C	O	N	V	E	N	E		A	R	G	O	N
	U		I		O		B			H		O
S	T	E	T		O	B	L	I	G	E		U
	L		I		K		A			T	A	G
R	E	I	N	D	E	E	R			T		A
	T		G		R		E	S	C	O	R	T

109

P	R	E	L	A	T	E		P	U	F	F	S
R		P		L				A		O		O
A	D	I	E	U		U	T	T	E	R	E	R
M		C		M		T		H		C		T
S	H	U	T		N	I	B		B	E	D	E
		R		M		L		M				R
W		E	R	A	D	I	C	A	T	E		S
O				N		S		P		V		
U	R	D	U		D	I	G		W	O	L	F
N		E		R		N		A		L		I
D	A	N	C	I	N	G		N	O	V	E	L
E		I		M				T		E		M
D	A	M	E	S		R	E	S	I	S	T	S

110

T	E	R	R	A	P	I	N		L	I	C	K
	V		A		E		A		O		R	
C	A	E	S	A	R		S	A	B	R	E	S
	S		P		J	E	T		E		P	
P	I	T	Y		U		Y	E	L	L	E	D
	O				R				I			
U	N	D	U	L	Y		C	L	A	S	S	Y
			N				A				T	
S	P	O	U	T	S		R		E	X	I	T
	I		S		W	I	T		X		M	
E	X	C	U	S	E		O	U	T	P	U	T
	I		A		E		N		R		L	
H	E	E	L		T	A	S	M	A	N	I	A

111

U	N	B	E	N	T		L	O	N	E	L	Y
P				I		S		N				E
L		C	A	T	A	C	L	Y	S	M		O
I		A		R		R		X		U		M
F	A	C	T	I	O	U	S		I	S	L	E
T		O		T		M		S		I		N
	S	P	I	E	S		S	P	A	C	E	
B		H		S		R		R		I		G
E	G	O	S		R	E	L	O	C	A	T	E
A		N		F		C		C		N		N
K		Y	A	R	M	U	L	K	E	S		E
E				O		R		E				V
R	A	V	A	G	E		O	T	T	A	W	A

112

T	A	R	T	N	E	S	S		S	H	O	P
	U		H		N		W		Q		M	
P	R	E	Y	E	D		E	X	U	D	E	D
	I		M		E	T	A		E		G	
A	C	H	E		M		R	E	L	O	A	D
	L				I				C			
H	E	R	O	I	C		A	T	H	E	N	S
			P				M				U	
B	R	I	E	R	S		A		D	O	C	K
	E		R		H	I	T		E		L	
O	R	N	A	T	E		E	S	C	H	E	W
	U		T		L		U		A		A	
K	N	E	E		F	A	R	M	Y	A	R	D

113

M	O	D	E	S	T	Y		U	P	P	E	R
O		I		T				T		O		I
D	I	A	R	Y		D	I	A	L	L	E	D
E		M		E		R		H		K		D
L	I	O	N		T	O	P		R	A	I	L
		N		N		M		S				E
R		D	E	A	D	E	N	I	N	G		S
A				Y		D		T		R		
U	N	D	O		R	A	N		H	E	A	L
C		E		D		R		A		A		A
O	B	E	S	I	T	Y		G	A	S	E	S
U		M		A				E		E		T
S	I	S	A	L		N	U	D	I	S	T	S

114

Answers

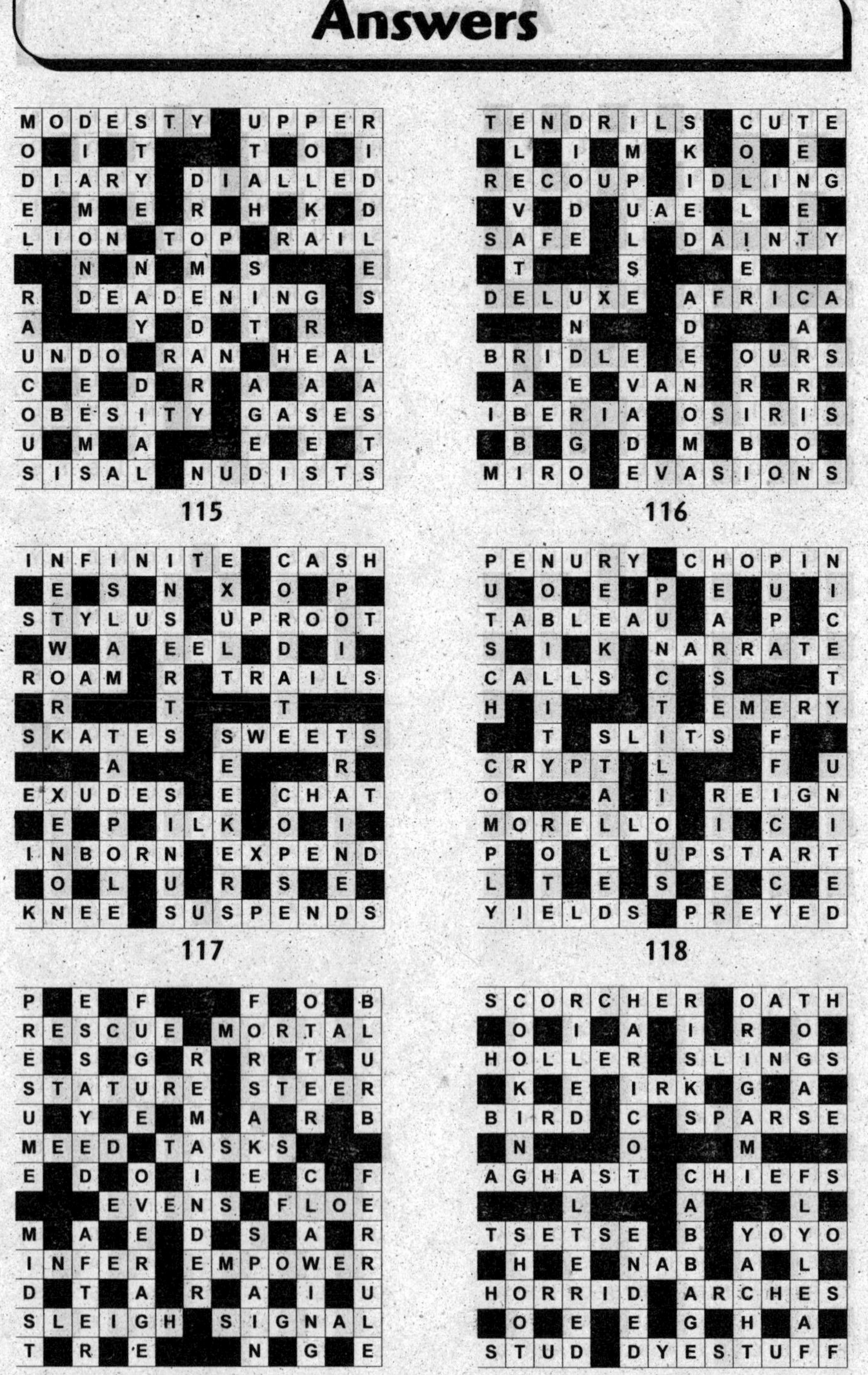

115

116

117

118

119

120

Answers

C	L	A	I	M	S		R	E	V	A	M	P
U				I		T		L				L
D		F	I	S	H	E	R	M	E	N		U
D		O		D		X		S		O		N
L	A	U	R	E	A	T	E		P	R	I	G
Y		N		E		S		A		M		E
	E	T	U	D	E		I	D	E	A	S	
A		A		S		U		M		T		S
B	R	I	G		I	N	C	I	S	I	O	N
S		N		S		I		R		V		O
U		S	Y	M	B	O	L	I	S	E		O
R				U		N		N				P
D	E	L	E	T	E		A	G	E	N	C	Y

121

F	L	O	C	K	E	D		B	U	G	L	E
I		U		N				E		R		P
L	A	T	H	E		C	A	R	R	O	T	S
T		L		E		R		N		U		I
H	U	E	S		N	O	R		O	P	A	L
		T		A		T		L				O
P		S	E	D	U	C	T	I	O	N		N
A				D		H		P		I		
R	A	N	D		W	E	T		O	B	E	Y
S		O		L		T		F		B		U
N	U	R	S	E	R	Y		L	I	L	A	C
I		S		G				A		E		C
P	L	E	A	S		J	A	K	A	R	T	A

122

A	D	V	I	C	E		E	S	S	A	Y	S
D				R		O		H				C
M		G	R	E	A	T	C	O	A	T		O
I		Y		D		H		E		E		L
T	A	M	P	E	R	E	D		A	M	I	D
S		N		N		R		S		P		S
	B	A	T	C	H		S	P	O	O	N	
S		S		E		C		R		R		S
T	W	I	N		P	L	E	A	S	A	N	T
O		U		E		E		Y		R		U
N		M	O	R	T	A	L	I	T	Y		P
E				A		T		N				O
S	T	R	E	S	S		U	G	L	I	E	R

123

B	L	U	D	G	E	O	N		I	D	E	A
	I		O		L		O		N		N	
S	T	R	I	D	E		R	A	V	I	N	E
	H		N		V	I	M		O		U	
K	I	N	G		A		S	P	I	R	I	T
	U				T				C			
I	M	B	I	B	E		S	L	E	E	V	E
			N				L				E	
B	L	U	F	F	S		E		P	O	R	K
	O		U		A	X	E		A		T	
O	F	F	S	E	T		P	U	N	D	I	T
	T		E		E		E		I		G	
G	Y	M	S		D	I	R	E	C	T	O	R

124

O	P	P	U	G	N		C	L	O	S	E	D
D				L		T		I				A
O		Q	U	A	D	R	I	L	L	E		M
U		U		Z		A		T		M		A
R	H	I	N	I	T	I	S		S	U	N	G
S		Z		E		T		T		L		E
	C	Z	A	R	S		C	H	E	S	S	
S		I		S		I		I		I		S
P	A	C	T		O	V	E	R	L	O	O	K
R		A		R		I		T		N		A
O		L	O	O	S	E	N	E	S	S		T
U				U		S		E				E
T	W	I	S	T	S		E	N	D	E	A	R

125

S		C		J				E		L		B
C	U	R	L	E	D		E	N	T	I	C	E
R		I		E		S		S		M		R
O	U	T	G	R	O	W		N	A	P	P	Y
L		I		S		A		A		S		L
L	O	C	K		C	L	E	R	K			
S		S		S		L		E		S		A
			S	T	R	O	P		L	I	O	N
A		B		I		W		M		L		O
S	W	U	N	G		E	G	O	T	I	S	T
I		R		M		D		C		C		H
D	E	N	T	A	L		T	H	R	O	N	E
E		T		S				A		N		R

126

Answers

P	I	G	E	O	N		U		A		C	
A		E			O	B	S	I	D	I	A	N
N	O	R			O		U		E		N	
D		B	I	C	K	E	R		N	O	A	H
E		I			S		P		O		R	
R	U	L	E	D		R	E	M	I	N	D	S
			F		C		D		D			
S	T	A	F	F	E	D		A	S	K	E	D
	E		I		R		M			E		I
T	A	L	C		T	H	E	I	S	T		A
	C		A		A		D			T	O	P
Z	U	C	C	H	I	N	I			L		E
	P		Y		N		A	R	R	E	A	R

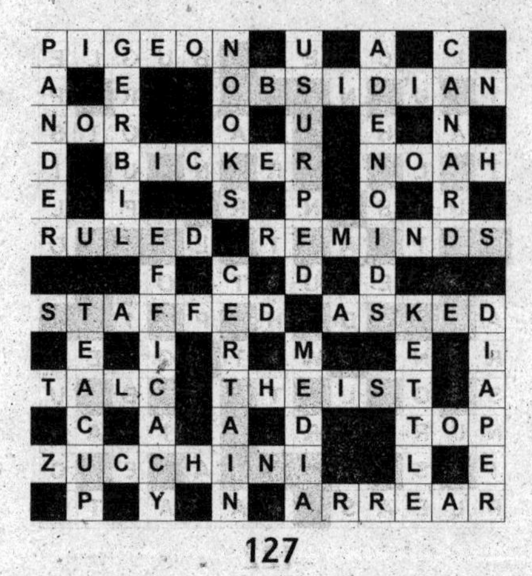

127

U	N	W	O	U	N	D		F	O	R	G	E
R		H		P				U		I		X
G	U	A	N	O		E	R	R	A	T	I	C
E		T		N		N		Y		E		E
D	A	N	E		S	U	M		U	S	E	R
		O		H		N		N				P
S		T	R	U	N	C	H	E	O	N		T
N				T		I		E		E		
I	O	N	S		S	A	T		S	T	I	R
P		O		S		T		E		T		E
P	R	O	V	I	D	E		T	A	L	O	N
E		N		P				O		E		T
T	E	S	T	S		S	I	N	U	S	E	S

128

B	A	C	K	U	P		A		A		S	
E		L			H	E	S	I	T	A	T	E
V	I	A			I		S		Y		A	
E		S	A	L	A	M	I		P	E	T	S
L		S			L		S		I		U	
S	T	Y	L	I		S	T	I	C	K	E	R
			U		E		S		A			
D	E	N	M	A	R	K		F	L	I	E	R
	U		I		U		B			S		I
I	R	A	N		D	R	O	V	E	S		V
	O		A		I		O			U	A	E
O	P	E	R	A	T	E	S			E		R
	E		Y		E		T	O	S	S	E	S

129

S		T		S				P		S		E
T	E	E	T	H	E		K	E	Y	P	A	D
R		A		O		C		N		E		I
E	N	C	L	O	S	E		C	R	A	F	T
T		H		T		M		I		R		S
C	A	E	N		R	E	A	L	M			
H		R		E		N		S		N		H
			O	M	I	T	S		S	O	D	A
S		S		B		I		U		T		N
T	W	I	L	L		N	E	S	T	I	N	G
A		L		E		G		H		C		M
S	A	L	A	M	I		S	E	R	E	N	A
H		Y		S				R		S		N

130

I	B	E	R	I	A		S	M	O	K	E	D
N		R		V		U		A		I		O
C	A	U	T	I	O	N		C		T		U
O		P		E		D	R	A	P	E	R	S
M	O	T	E	S		E		Q				E
E		I				S		U	R	G	E	D
		O		A	B	I	D	E		O		
L	I	N	E	R		R				R		S
E				O		A		B	O	G	E	Y
P	E	R	T	U	R	B		O		E		S
T		O		S		L	O	O	K	O	U	T
O		S		A		E		B		U		E
N	E	E	D	L	E		G	Y	P	S	U	M

131

P	E	R	M	U	T	E		C	O	C	O	A
U		E		S				L		A		S
L	I	T	R	E		P	R	O	M	P	T	S
S		U		D		O		T		E		A
E	A	R	N		A	L	L		E	D	G	Y
		N		G		A		F				E
P		S	Q	U	I	R	M	I	N	G		R
I				Y		I		T		U		
M	A	I	L		A	S	S		K	N	O	W
P		D		T		E		G		S		I
L	E	O	P	A	R	D		A	B	H	O	R
E		L		X				L		O		E
S	U	S	H	I		S	H	A	T	T	E	R

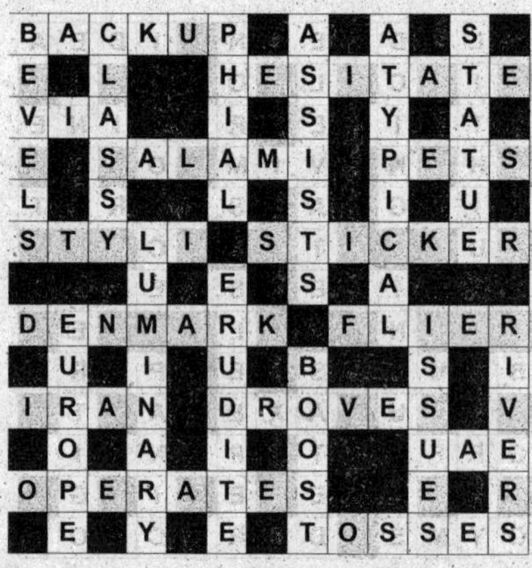

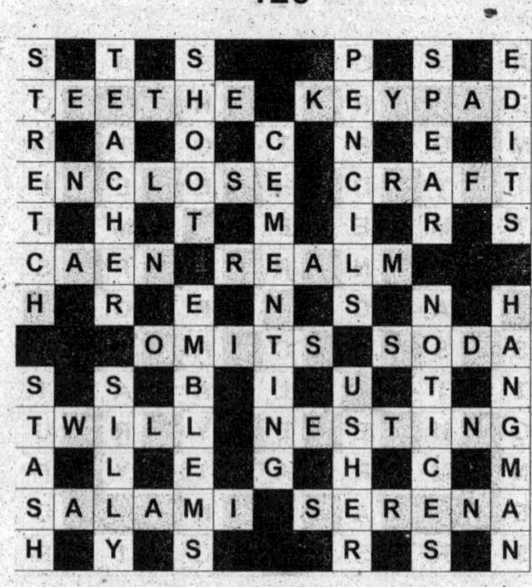

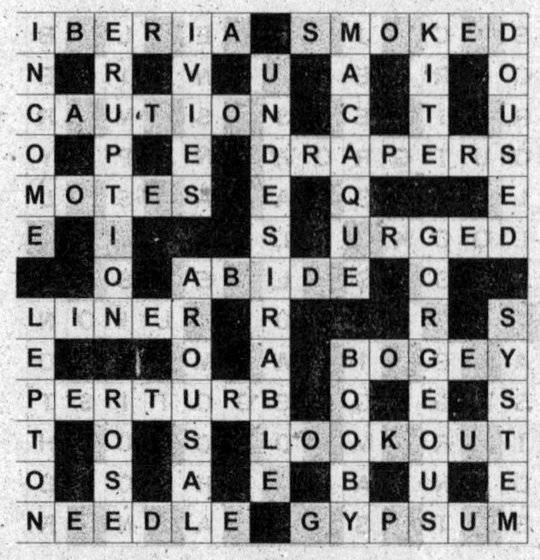

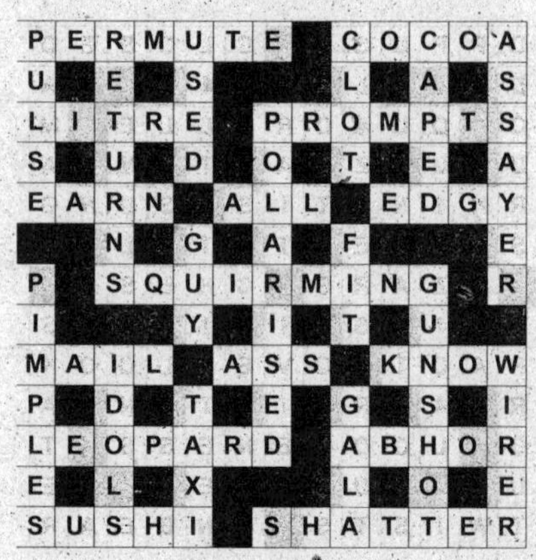

132

Answers

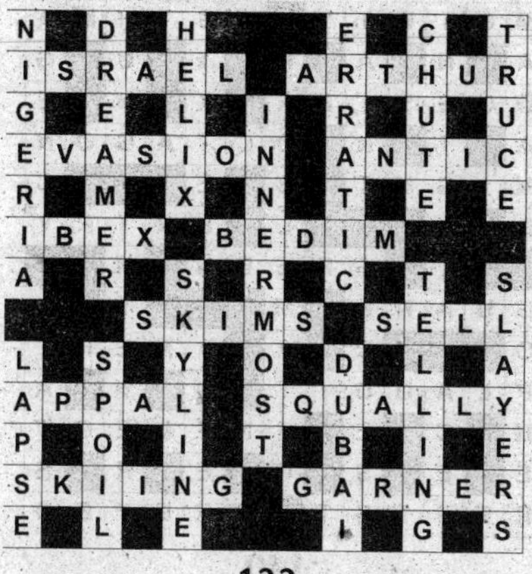

133

L	A	U	G	H	S		A	S	S	A	Y	S
O				A		A		P				E
U		H	A	R	D	S	H	I	P	S		S
N		O		D		K		N		U		A
G	R	U	M	B	L	E	S		P	R	I	M
E		S		A		D		C		V		E
	B	E	E	C	H		O	L	D	E	N	
I		M		K		O		U		Y		E
S	W	A	P		C	R	I	M	P	I	N	G
O		I		S		I		S		N		O
B		D	E	P	L	O	R	I	N	G		I
A				O		N		E				S
R	E	C	I	T	E		T	R	U	I	S	M

134

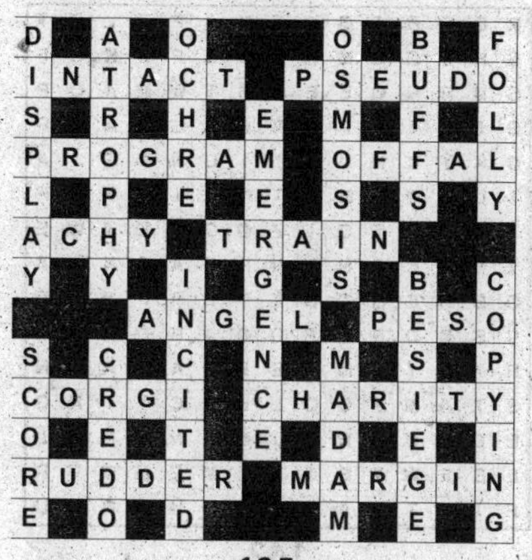

135

B	U	B	B	L	E		A		L		I	
A		U			A	U	C	T	I	O	N	S
L	A	D			R		A		F		T	
T		D	E	P	E	N	D		E	P	E	E
I		H			D		E		L		N	
C	H	A	F	F		A	M	N	E	S	T	Y
			U		C		Y		S			
B	E	L	G	I	U	M		P	S	A	L	M
	Y		I		I		G			B		U
R	E	N	T		S	O	N	A	T	A		T
	L		I		I		A			T	A	U
S	E	R	V	I	N	G	S			E		A
	T		E		E		H	A	N	D	E	L

136

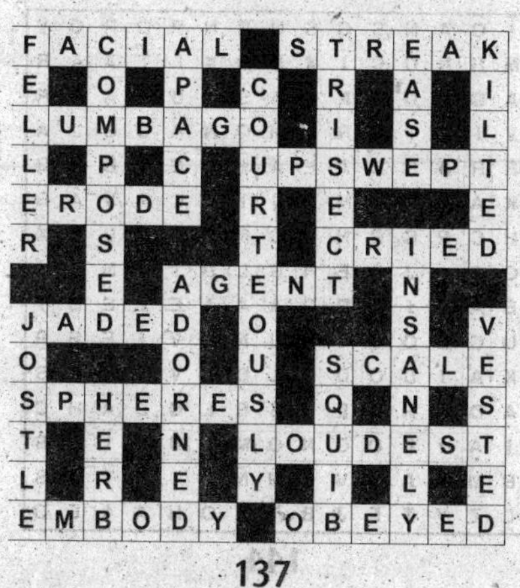

137

S	T	E	R	E	O		S		M		R	
A		X			P	E	C	T	O	R	A	L
T	O	E			T		R		N		I	
U		M	I	N	I	M	A		R	U	S	E
R		P			C		P		O		I	
N	O	T	E	S		S	E	R	V	A	N	T
			V		S		D		I			
D	E	F	E	C	T	S		C	A	P	E	S
	Q		N		A		T			E		L
T	U	F	T		R	O	O	K	I	E		O
	I		F		T		K			L	I	P
A	N	N	U	A	L	L	Y			E		P
	E		L		E		O	S	P	R	E	Y

138

Answers

R	I	S	S	O	L	E	S		C	O	K	E
	N		A		E		T		A		N	
A	G	E	N	D	A		U	N	C	L	O	G
	R		D		T	O	N		K		B	
L	E	V	Y		H		G	A	L	O	S	H
	S				E				E			
U	S	U	R	E	R		I	N	S	U	R	E
			O				T				E	
A	B	S	O	R	B		C		F	A	W	N
	E		S		A	A	H		E		R	
C	L	O	T	H	S		I	G	L	O	O	S
	L		E		T		N		O		T	
R	E	A	R		E	N	G	I	N	E	E	R

139

M	O	I	E	T	Y		A	S	T	H	M	A
A		N		A		P		I		U		G
D	O	S	S	I	E	R		X		N		E
A		I		N		O	C	T	A	G	O	N
M	I	G	H	T		B		E				C
E		N				L		E	N	T	R	Y
		I		G	R	E	E	N		H		
G	U	A	N	O		M				I		S
O				D		A		I	N	E	R	T
P	L	A	U	D	I	T		N		V		A
H		C		E		I	N	F	L	E	C	T
E		E		S		C		E		R		E
R	E	S	I	S	T		P	R	E	Y	E	D

140

C		W		B				P		S		U
R	E	I	N	E	D		T	R	A	C	E	S
U		G		A		U		A		R		A
N	E	W	S	M	E	N		Y	O	U	N	G
C		A		S		D		E		B		E
H	E	M	S		B	E	A	R	D			
Y		S		O		R		S		C		E
			I	R	I	S	H		B	O	O	N
A		J		I		H		M		N		V
W	R	O	N	G		O	D	Y	S	S	E	Y
A		L		I		T		T		I		I
R	E	L	E	N	T		C	H	O	S	E	N
E		Y		S				S		T		G

141

R	D	O	B	A	Q	U	T	U	I	F	U	L	R	T
G	H	C	G	R	M	H	B	D	E	F	X	K	O	F
S	U	R	N	G	E	E	A	S	T	W	M	A	O	P
D	I	K	I	P	P	W	N	C	R	G	O	A	G	R
O	K	Y	K	H	U	G	I	I	U	N	V	S	I	A
I	U	B	O	O	M	N	T	N	C	I	I	F	R	R
T	W	O	O	T	O	I	Z	O	G	C	E	T	W	E
Y	E	A	C	O	N	T	N	R	E	A	S	N	A	A
O	B	R	C	G	T	U	X	T	E	R	P	N	L	D
U	S	D	D	R	O	P	O	C	J	R	O	R	K	I
R	I	G	I	A	M	M	S	E	Y	A	R	A	I	N
S	T	A	M	P	C	O	L	L	E	C	T	I	N	G
E	E	M	U	H	R	C	J	E	S	N	S	R	G	L
L	S	E	W	Y	R	T	S	I	M	E	H	C	V	R
F	I	S	T	F	A	R	C	I	S	U	M	R	L	U

142

T	Y	S	S	T	H	E	C	R	O	S	S	A	Q	R
S	R	A	B	T	H	E	R	A	I	L	W	A	Y	O
R	S	D	N	U	O	H	D	N	A	X	O	F	O	Y
A	S	A	A	T	P	U	N	I	C	O	R	N	U	A
G	A	E	P	E	T	H	E	C	H	U	R	C	H	L
L	P	H	V	W	H	I	T	E	B	E	A	R	E	S
A	M	S	R	E	T	S	E	R	O	F	E	H	T	T
F	O	G	A	Y	E	T	G	N	T	Y	E	S	T	A
A	C	A	R	O	S	E	A	N	D	C	R	O	W	N
R	E	N	B	S	P	M	R	S	I	L	H	P	Z	D
T	H	E	R	O	Y	A	L	O	A	K	T	G	K	A
E	T	H	E	C	R	I	C	K	E	T	E	R	S	R
H	D	T	H	E	S	Q	U	A	R	E	S	H	D	D
T	C	V	G	C	R	O	W	A	N	D	G	A	T	E
Q	G	S	A	O	R	P	J	S	T	A	A	N	W	O

143

I	O	A	N	S	G	S	U	R	N	P	O	R	O	Y
M	H	N	O	C	I	X	E	M	A	L	T	A	A	R
A	Q	A	U	C	K	H	A	S	Y	U	A	A	X	R
V	I	P	I	L	R	L	M	O	N	A	C	O	J	A
R	R	A	S	B	A	E	A	F	E	G	I	D	N	B
K	A	J	B	Y	M	B	J	I	K	C	R	V	A	B
H	C	R	S	R	N	A	O	N	E	O	F	U	L	X
O	S	I	J	O	E	N	G	L	D	I	A	N	G	J
B	A	B	I	C	D	O	A	A	I	E	Z	E	B	T
U	G	E	O	C	T	N	U	N	F	V	I	E	E	R
K	A	I	D	O	D	C	L	D	P	V	I	H	Q	S
A	D	S	R	R	E	V	S	R	L	Q	D	A	H	C
I	A	I	L	O	G	N	O	M	A	D	R	I	D	R
B	M	V	A	M	V	B	M	N	P	I	B	T	A	S
L	Z	Y	T	E	J	B	T	Z	O	H	A	I	E	O

144

Answers

```
O X Q S Q E S L Z S S W R T R
G O I O N M A T C H T F Q F S
O I N E V O P O E S S B W R R
U E I E J W O L G U L T I W S
I A O C E P F P H S U F A S E
B U T T E R D I S H X U A R V
W Q X O V B U U I S T A K D T
B A R P A R O T D O O R R D R
N P V W W E E X G T C E L C S
E Y P E O C L N N H P T W Q R
M J H T R I D E I U N S O D L
Q G P S C L N N V A L A F O V
I F K N I S A T R E R O A U Q
M E R E M A C R E M I T G G E
K Z I L U Q L A S O T S S H O
```

145

```
Y G T W S J S T N J A T A R Z
P B T E A S P Z U S A L O Y R
S U R L M L A J K W I H V S S
R T E O P O K R I I S T A W S
R T E Z O J Z E G N E A O K A
B E S D U K W C R G E P O T Z
Q R I A H S E R F S S T O D F
L C E R U T N E V D A O A V L
E U A E R A Y A L P W O A A O
U P S T T B U T T E R F L Y W
Q Z H A U E P I G E O N S P E
R N R W R N D O G W A L K E R
K T U O B A D N U O R U A O S
P A B T A O J R L E P O F Z L
P E S T A T E A B I B U G Y U
```

146

```
T D I T M D J B E R U H V O A
Y S N L A J O N A H K Z E W T
F A I O L A P O C S I P E S G
C B D D M T S I N I V L A C R
U M N S O R W T R E H S O K E
R B R O M H O P N H T A B C E
D O V U I O T M S Q R L A H K
P C U D F T O E K S H V R R O
M A N N A R A D M E V A M I R
Q J O H N T H E B A P T I S T
H O L Y Y E A R R P A I T T H
P A R A B L E Y R C Y O Z I O
U E B M E W S L Y T U N V A D
S T V W S F A L L O F M A N O
J Z O R E O W Z A R S M H H X
```

147

```
S I E A N C S M O K E F S U S
R S L U E J O P E T P Y A F R
L R B P E X T U R A J R O I I
L J B S N O F R G E C A T R R
A F U G I M I E S H A I T E A
I X R D G U W H G M I D V M J
A O N O N W A S M R W N I A I
Z F I R E B R I G A D E G N T
E P N H E A M U M L A C E A G
S G G R R T T G B A P N T O T
T J R S I A H N O I T I N G I
A L O R F D R I R E N C Z A Q
S N P E E U T T Y G A S H E S
P K L V S J I X W D A N G E R
T S T E W A T E R I F N O B S
```

148

```
W R R S T U O R P S Q R A L I
D C T C O U R G E T T E X Y T
I R D A N D E L I O N I O N N
J E A F C P A I L O C C O R B
R S X H U C R J C H I C O R Y
A S E C C E T G E S R L B R C
T S C A U L I F L O W E R G O
H J U B M E C Q E O M N O R C
E O T B B R H T R B A N A U P
N D T A E Y O C I M N E D L R
X D E G R V K E A A U F B S S
S O L E Y I E V C B G R E T O
E A D A H V I I S A U C A S U
R F D J Y V G H E R K I N L L
F T S R Q T C C S X Q A P L K
```

149

```
W K L C A C H E S A B A T A D
W C C O N T R O L K E Y R O C
L D Y M F U R Y R G U H M H L
W P E M I T S S E C C A A E O
J D N A B D A O R B I R S U C
W Y C N E T A L U N A D D R O
B A U D R A T E N C P D L I T
U Q X P M A E A T T O R Y S O
L U X R O I M E X R T I H T R
G H P O U E R P A C K V C I P
S B W M S S A R M W S E T C F
I H Y P E R T E X T E A N T L
M U L T I T H R E A D I N G T
H E T T E L E L L A R A P U A
I T Y U I O L T E A T I S P Q
```

150

Answers

T S I T R A S R P W R S V D P
A N I M A L S L L L C L U N M
C K E M I M O T N A P E A U J
F I L M Q O U U I S E M S U O
L C A N N O N R M E Z A G D S
M T E C H I L D R E N G B R Y
S R L C A Y A E L J L I I M R
C A C U R O D T E E Z C G A A
L P Y S A X W A R H U I D P S
P E C T Z S O S U E W A I N T
T Z I A A C R O B A T N P B W
A E N R O S C E J W A N P M O
R E U D R I N G M A S T E R H
T E K C U B I G T O P L R L P
P L T U T C L O W N S A U Y F

151

W L R I T L U E V B W K A W V
A L W D N A S Z B R P V K L I
V D I J S R O I A Q W T E O E
E A P M A O S C R D D M Y R U
S G S O P C K E N T P U U A M
E A R H L E Q C A I O X N K L
A A Y L E Y T R C W F S D A M
N T C O K M P E L F E F V K P
E N O M E N A A E S K E U K I
T F T P Y G O M R Y R R D P Y
T R E W W C N S H Y I T I S I
L L U G A E S O T P L X U H K
E T I G N U F H P Z L T B M L
E G T V X R L E S S U M N W I
M M T X W S L Q L S Q K R A A

152

Y S B S O G R U Y T S V T C J
G N I T E K C A R B U L B P X
D O C A B L E R E L E A S E P
U I W C C A M E R A F S G T V
F S F L I O L C R C A G R R G
G L S F N O O T E K S N U D T
G U B O U N O I T A T I G A C
A M I P T S N A L N F S I Y A
P E S R R H E L I D I O E L P
E R A S P K P R F W L P U I M
R S W O L L E B I H M X L G O
T U C E L L U L O I D E O H C
U D L E I F F O H T P E D T A
R K S Y G C L O S E U P U Z D
E P W D E V E L O P R I E B T

153

I H R S V M O T Q U E X C W N
O J N A B Y K P X C R O I D T
P L G J N A I A Q P P E H K I
L D L S H Q C T P K Q O S H R
T R T E N A T S A C P P S A S
M U B P C F R E N C H H O R N
E M U I N O H P U E A A N M R
M S G P O L Y I S E O B O O E
I P L N O O R P A I T I I N M
R E E A S C R G M S C L D I I
D H N P S C N A G R O H R U C
A S O J A I N B I O A V O M L
T Z F O B P A T S E L E C R U
G I F P F A S L A B M Y C A D
C V Q W Z P E K E Y B O A R D

154

S R Y T M B E T H A T X I I V
B A Y F J B C X J B A S M T V
A B R O Q H O I A S G M D U S
B A R A C K J R E S A C U C X
E N A A B N R T I G I E P I H
S R B T D R S A S S X Y P E C
E B R B I L A E S P A C L S O
F E C N O Y E B Q T Q A I T B
R N A I A O T Y C U O Y P Q T
W I D M R P T I P R S R R B J
I T N A T O D H B L I S A B F
P O I J B E R T I E K I E A E
H I L N N O E V S H C L D G S
I X E E S E T E Z O L K A X A
V S B B A L T A S A R W Y Y Z

155

D T R Y A W M D Y S A T N A F
H R O A L D E F R I E N D S E
Q E E C K T R S A A P G P I R
T N A T M P Y E T E M F O S R
J O E R S X T D N E S A P Q O
U I E E T U P W E A R U C S S
E T I S R T B T M M L N O E S
O C R S A C H K U K O I R Z L
M I E E I M S R C A E C N J X
T F H S L Z N E O O W Q N E S
R D S R E L O K D B L O S R R
Y U U O R L I N E I P B M E W
M G Q T S P T R I T W R E L I
Z U R C A S C I H O R R O R U
B F K A S T A E S T Q L H A Z

156

Answers

D U N B A R T O N S H I R E W
O V D U M F R I E S S H I R E
A Z C J U L X R R S B P Z I R
S [illegible] I K T P Z J Y E W R L H I
M O R A Y S H I R E I O D S H
I I N V E R N E S S E S N N S
D I V N A I H T O L T S A E N
L S S T I R L I N G I S L E R
O P I X J O R K N E Y H T D I
T P E R T H S H I R E I E R A
H E F H S W W U Q M S R H E N
I P I B U T E S H I R E S B G
A A F P E R I H S K R A N A L
N T C A I T H N E S S U G N A
K T V I I B E R W I C K N V S

157

S Q A E N W T T F U S N P S R
A E Z R S Q A R T D O I I P O
U S H A L I X T Z R E V L I S
T N I T A R R N F A T I S N Q
F K M L S C H E S T N U T K C
R W F A T B M C C S A I P O I
T A E B L E A S Y U D V P S R
T K L O U R R E A M R P U G F
U U N C M R M R N E E P U C R
W D B I V E G O A R V V E R Q
M X N G R R R U G C L D U E N
I E N A V Y B L N R O K U A X
D W L V F W S F U D E T Y M M
A D R P T G A T I C Y E T R D
M H O B X O H G S I E N N A U

158

I I Q M P K O S R E T S I N A
P H S N J Z L J S A Z F Y L L
I A F I R Q B S O A C A R U C
Y P U H K I R S C H E T R S O
V A U L G R E N A D I N E C H
P K C N M E T A L O C O H C O
X O X H C H A R T R E U S E L
C I D E R H W I O Y L R F H I
G W Y R A M Y D O O L B M L A
S G O B E N E D I C T I N E T
W O O A P P L E J A C K T C K
B U L L B W R M L N U S R C C
M D O T S C A P P U C C I N O
K N N E T A B S I N T H E Q C
E N G A P M A H C S V J Y D A

159

U I O U U A W E D V U C C U A
A F N R O H T K C U B M U N U
I O O B M A B D I L L A I R A
T N A E L K W O O D U S Y U F
Z S U R A T L O H Q E L S O I
V F U O P U S W H E S A L B R
E E V H Y T S N D S P B W M T
B P C P R U E E T P R R A A R
S I Q M O N K E Y P U Z Z L E
U Y R A V T F R R Q C U A A E
X H L C I S T G M T E P I C J
J J X R H E L C A P M A H C N
R E B M A H O G A N Y L F U L
Y R R E H C R E D C E D A R S
S S J S A A H R K W T A K P Q

160

U T U S U R T U K F T L N P D
B U G S L O O P M A H S R U L
K S T N E C S L A B R E H I K
X L O T I O N T Y M H I L T S
C I T S A S T C S C T R O B M
A O A S L E W O T T A T S W H
N R N T S S A A P U B E T M O
D E U D H K R A W B E L L G E
L D A O I C R E A M L I P S X
E N W V S T O S S E B O O A Y
S E Y K D R I Z H X B T V S R
R V C A N N O O I S U I T R Y
H A I R C A R E N I B E T L R
B L A Q S P O N G E A C S P Q
Q Q L P R E T A W M R A W K M

161

T P A Y I A G U E J N N P G H
R I Y R R E B N A R C L T Z C
E N I R A T C E N A R O Y D K
N E Z E E L P P A B A R C K I
I A I B L A C K B E R R Y Y G
R P V E M G R A P E F R U I T
E P S S I Y H Y B P R U N E G
G L A O P Y R R E B E U L B A
N E V O U B E R D H Y H T J G
A L O G A D S E E P D N S L R
T Y C N L I R H U B A R B W C
O M A E M R H C U A L V N P B
A N D M A N D A R I N U F I S
A C O C O N U T T A U Q M U K
P N C R P S S I B D L L Y I Z

162

Answers

K A D Q E C O U C H C I T P R
R S S R O R R I M U X S P G T
S R E W A R D F O T S E H C F
W T Q D W O L L I P Q H E D L
G X T N G R B X Y T W U I C U
D X O L E N A P A O U E A O M
D S N A X A I B U C B N L E N
I N T X U M L T P C D L L T F
W M A N T E L P I E C E L P I
Z I H T L N B R L R D R O A T
L T W A S T I A Q O W R T A T
L R M A Q P B I S E T T E E I
P P H T J R M A X K A Y Y E N
T E P R A C M A L X E M K W G
Q D F Z X A O R L O O T S G S

163

C A M P U S E Y T P P L U S D
M T M O T R C P E R O J A M U
T A O A N S P U P I L C B Q N
Z U O R R I Q O T M H J R A C
X O R P O S T G R A D U A T E
J Q S O I E T O L R D L L L E
B S S P T H L K R Y I A O T V
W G A P R C S C U G S L H U H
E T L S I I E W A L C S C S R
L O C T M M Z P O P I C S F O
W L S L E L F E S L P A R J M
Z X O T S N C S T N L I N E S
L N O I T I U T L L I E J V I
U P A P E R I J I F N A F A C
B V D A R Y O B D A E H L N U

164

C I J E O U I U D S S D C U Y
S C A R B A S P O L K A B G H
V X O P L I H E B P B N L Z F
X P N N V A U R M R P S J S Z
M Z E P G R F H I U B E O K A
A P P I A A F O L E R U M B A
L E R R A B L I B S W R B G S
O Z T O L E E O A E H T L J D
V G L U L S P H R K G I V M F
A L S E T Q K L N C S U M J X
T G U T H U R E D S A A I M W
U N O T S E L R A H C Z E N Y
T S Y E T D T D N R R L I J E
I V Q Q J F E M C A N C A N S
G P J G J I T T E R B U G U L

165

R I G P B I M I Y W T X L B K
S A E T I H T S O T T C I O U
M O O L A I U T O N I B L H U
S O R L N R W U N A J Y S M R
Y N G Q L I E L B U O R C F T
E G E P V Q X T U Y P E S O L
G I N N E F P C R O W N A F R
X E O I L X P E E A Q D N T I
F R B E L B T E P R U P I A H
S E L K N R A P P R E Q C M A
U V E K C E E Q O R T Y K S E
V O D D I E U T C S Z U E O K
S S Y O I I P M S D A S L N F
Q Q S K D N U O P A L A D L S
R U Z L O U D E C N E R O L F

166

L K V A D E C D L D X U C U P
P C E X F O H O N O R I U S L
L A A R E N C P O M P E Y F U
F T B L P R E S U I R E B I T
P I K T I Y X R F T H I Q T A
H T N S E G E E V I A E S A R
I U A A C V U K S A D B U U C
L S L R N G A L G N R G S J H
I U O N E R O T A C I T U S E
P T C N R D G A L B A A A I X
P S I O E L F U L S N T G O I
U U R E T P S X U C Y J A P B
S G G Q R M R T S O Q B A A L
A U A L K R W S A S R P Q M T
N A J A R T I A B N T H L R U

167

I F X T E H R E F I E H O W S
U T B D R A Y E N I V N I A R
N T E F E R T I L I Z E R S L
L R P T H V C M B L S A M X S
F U I N S E C T I C I D E Y T
I W P O E S P W S R R T I U R
T R U I R T E A F O Y O B S A
A L E T H I J G S A P E P X W
W H E A T N U O S T R M A S T
A U S V T G K N K I U M O P B
R U V I T I C U L T U R E C A
Q R T T C D C O M B I N E R A
C H A L R K R S I M R T F G U
E U U U P A L A S N I Q Z D K
A R E C H W O E A E S E P T V

168

Answers

```
O M E T N H E N A G O N U L S
P V R L O T F A W O C P K A I
Q C N O G A T N E P T S U I E
S U I O Y N H E P T A G O N C
I T C K L M A G L A G Z R M R
N T O D O M H T N G O K E S E
E S S K P U M R C U N L A Q S
Q U A D R I L A T E R A L U C
H B G T Y Z H P J P R I I A E
E M O L S E S E J O R T R R N
K O N P X P K Z G L V P R E T
U H Q A H A D O D E C A G O N
S R G E N R C I R C L E L O T
A O R K I T E D Y V M H P Z T
N E Y X K M U D N P R A S T E
```

169

```
K D A L E M U R P H Y H P O F
J A N S R E N K C U B L L I B
I R G D U K E S N I D E R L F
M R E J R E S I E R E T E P Q
M Y L G S S A F X H E O D R T
O L B R I H E N R Y A A R O N
R K E J S A M O H T K N A R F
R I R S Y N P T L L E B B U H
I L R S N I L L O C E I D D E
S E O J H T U R E B A B Y O L
F R A S E C R A G H C I R S I
R K A S U I S C B E C C T A E
A L K A L I N E C Q Z T U T N
J I C O R B S E H C K C A J B
R E B U R G A D D I E J O S S
```

170

```
W L L S J O A M P L I T U D E
K P H B I G B A N G Y O R I C
T A C T F B I G U D T N G W R
S R N L H D H N L Y I T R G O
E T U E M N Y E W N V S S M F
P I R M U M O T D A I Y B L G
D C C I T S M I I M T L U S R
P L G S N E R S T I A X O M A
T E I S A G N M V C L X N I V
P S B I U B T E K O E S U G I
L N O O Q D C H R U R V V T T
E O T N B T O B E G A I N V Y
R T K J O L I S A O Y A S O Z
P X L R E T T A M K R A D I C
U H S T R E N T R O P Y I K I
```

171

```
B H A R T I C L E V I S S A P
Y O F H P A R G I D T H A A B
J G G A W V F K E T L D O Z S
P D D I P H T H O N G D C R L
A E I D I L T O M O Y E O E R
P R M E P N O M I N A T I V E
C I P C Y T R O W C I C A I F
L V E L P L U P E R F E C T L
A A R A E N O H P O L L A A E
U T A R V D U O P S I F O L X
S I T A C O G N A T E N R B I
E V I T A D H O C T L I S A V
Q E V I T A S U C C A R Q A E
C P E V I T I S N A R T N I R
H L B E V I T A C I D N I B J
```

172

```
E L I R S Q Z W S D X L A L F
P P C R S V I R L S A S R R M
A U A G N I L C Y C Y E R R F
U G L N Z S C I B O R E A J Y
H N O I T A T P M E T S U O I
O I R M R V E E S L A O G R D
O P I M G E S I G S H A W I X
D A E I T E S I C R E X E T D
I H S W R T T K L E A S I P I
E S A S A J Q X O H L T G P Q
T P G N I T A E W S T H H Q U
I B C G N I D I R R H N T R B
N E S L I M M I N G Y K S S W
G N I N N U R H T H V O S C U
R G N I G G O J Z R D W T D R
```

173

```
T P E E P T O E M T S S R S E
Y A N S R E N I A R T Z S K T
A S T P A S A N S U O I L S K
P Y P A X D O L T O O P A Q A
Q L U D W T A E E C B P D A G
E L Q R N I S A C C O M N K M
T E O I B I G T T E L L A B H
R W A L K I N G S H O E S B P
S P O L F P I L F P R X L Y U
G O O E R B K M F J U R M U R
O N C I I R C T W A V D Z I M
L Z I K L L O S M I L P L C A
C O T D S Y T O V H U E R O T
R E P P I L S N E A K E R O H
S J H F I R M U S Y E O M P L
```

174

Answers

P T S S E L H T U R T S R T A
G L Z G E Z A E T A G P U R Q
S R N I A T P A C N G E D T F
X Y I H M R I O U S W A G U K
X L W O M E R R E V L I S E I
U L D S O G A I L V Y O V P D
J O O T S O T L T G I U Y J N
U P R A N R E Y E P A T C H A
E Y I G A Y S R E N O S I R P
Z T C E R L H P O B S T O P M
T T H S G L I P D R O P V T U
E E E F G O P K A L P U U P T
M R S P O J L O L V O S N P I
Z P I E C E S O F E I G H T N
K I W A L K T H E P L A N K Y

175

W R R M A O N S U P M G S H Z
B N A U R S B D E T A R G A H
Q B L U E T L Z G A D U O G E
M A L W Y I N G R P E Y A F U
X W E N S L E Y D A L E A Q T
E I R B C T L K X A G R E E K
B R A A K O E I C O M E M V C
R P Z A D N I S H H A D M H K
I A Z T M D C T O P A R E I M
C N O P R U E U I X R S N T X
O E M A G G S H E E H E T P Q
T E I P U E T I C I Y L A G M
T R O F U A E B R S U E L C I
A T E L J T R E B M E M A C F
A N J L J O F U J W P M S T E

176